"Anne Hargrove's 'conversations' with herself and other friends consist of twenty-five self-contained vignettes that convey briskly and wittily her experience with life-threatening breast cancer. Her stories surprise and delight the reader at every turn.

"Anne's work convincingly demonstrates the power of narrative to interpret and order the experience of sickness in life-enhancing ways. Clinicians who read Ann Hargrove's 'conversations' are likely to listen attentively to what their patients are trying to tell them."

William J. Donnelly, M.D.
Professor of Medicine, Loyola University,
Stritch School of Medicine

Consultant, Humanities and Ethics,
Edward Hines, Jr., Hospital,
Veterans Administration,
Hines, Illinois

Getting Better

Anne C. Hargrove, Ph.D.

Illustrations by Catherine Nye Petterson

CompCare Publishers, Minneapolis, Minnesota

Hargrove, Anne C.
    Getting better: conversations with myself and other friends while healing from
breast cancer / Anne C. Hargrove.

        p.   cm.
    ISBN 0-89638-145-5 : $8.95
    1. Hargrove, Anne C.—Health. 2. Breast—Cancer—Patients—United States—
Biography. 3. Breast—Cancer—Psychological aspects. I. Title.
RC280.B8H37 1988
362.1′96994—dc19
[B]   88-9585
                                          CIP

Illustrations by Catherine Nye Petterson
Cover design by Jeremy Gale
Interior design by Pamela Arnold

Inquiries, orders, and catalog requests should be addressed to
CompCare Publishers
2415 Annapolis Lane
Minneapolis, Minnesota 55441
Call toll free 800/328-3330
(Minnesota residents 612/559-4800)

    6   5   4   3   2
   93   92   91   90   89   88

For Andrew, my son

Contents

Author's Preface

When you are forty-one, a single parent of a young son and are told that you have breast cancer and that it has spread quite a bit from the breast to the lymph nodes nearby, you feel, sometimes, as if you are a character in someone else's book. That's how I felt, anyway. And suddenly it was very important to me to make whatever life I had left MY life. It wasn't long before I realized, though, that some changes were going to have to be made—changes in seeing, thinking, and feeling, for example. Changes in the way I organized my time. Could I handle changing and illness?

You bet! Being blessed with a sense of the ridiculous made it easier than it might have been. I suddenly saw how silly I looked as a character in other people's "books" and how silly most of us look when we live and die according to someone else's script. I wanted to get better not only physically but, as Kurt Vonnegut says, everywhichway.

Getting Better is about three things. It is about dealing with the physical, emotional, and spiritual trauma of serious illness. It is about discovering the deepest center of what a person calls "self," and maintaining a sense of integrity throughout a health crisis. And it is about the importance of staying in touch with life and with other people, especially the ones you care about and who care for you.

I tell a lot about myself in this book. In fact, people who have heard me read from it have often asked me how I can reveal such personal things. I tell them that, with Carl Rogers, I truly believe that what is most personal is most universal.

Writing *Getting Better* began as self-therapy. Then I showed my work to others to help them talk to me. And it worked! I hope those who read *Getting Better* now will share the chapters with each other. I hope they will be able to laugh and cry and talk to each other better about things personal and universal. And I hope they will all begin to get better everywhichway, too.

Anne Hargrove

Acknowledgments

I would like my readers to meet those who helped me write this book.

In the beginning were the English teachers at East High School in Wichita, who taught me to write and to want to write: Nancy Millett, Jeanne Ponds, and Elfreida Shellenberger. George Levine, Robert S. Davis, and Charles Forker at Indiana University fine-tuned my writing skills. Without these six people, this book would be a lot less fun to read.

Before I wrote *Getting Better* I had written only for myself and other academics. I knew nothing about getting a book like this into the hands of the public. I knew something about networking, though, so I wrote to Stephanie Simonton and asked for her help. Without her practical and friendly support in the early stages, *Getting Better* might never have found a publisher. In fact, without *Getting Well Again*, the book she co-authored with O. Carl Simonton, M.D., this book might never have been written. The editors at Round Tree Press were other friendly strangers who helped keep up my spirits while I sought a publisher.

I can't say enough good things about my agent, Jane Jordan Browne, who believed in my book from the beginning. My readers should admire her courage and perspicuity—and that of CompCare Publishers—for taking on what agents and publishers three years ago were nervously calling "a cancer book."

Jane Noland, my editor, has been infinitely patient, tactful, and meticulous. I promised her I would take responsibility for any grammatical or syntactical errors and I here claim poetic license for all of them.

Mary Byers was the friend into whose very reliable hands I entrusted the typing of my manuscript. I hope her new boss in Yuma appreciates what a real treasure she is. While I was writing and revising, my friends Jeanne Larkin, Maurine Magliocco, and Elvy O'Brien were a willing and empathetic audience. My friend Lorraine Schwartz also spent many hours helping me proofread.

My mother and father, Beth-Anne and Fred Chard, and my brothers and sisters, Kathy, Fred, David, and Martha, and my sister-in-law, Rainbow, enthusiastically encouraged me throughout and never failed to laugh in the right places. My eleven-year-old son, Andrew, has helped me in many ways, but especially by being himself, telling me the truth, and sometimes surprising me with breakfast in bed.

I am grateful for the encouragement of Dr. Paul Carbone of the University of Wisconsin Cancer Center and for the warmth and kindness of my own physicians, Rodger Lefler and Michael Veeder, who read my manuscript and who have never treated me as a "potentially dead person." Dr. William Donnelly, Loyola School of Medicine, has also been a good friend to me and allowed me to read from *Getting Better* to the very responsive and sensitive third-year class at Loyola. Writers need real audiences to talk to and I am also grateful that the Society for Health and Human Values afforded me an opportunity to read at their annual meeting.

You will run into Jeff Black many times in *Getting Better*. I'm sure glad I ran into him! He was my pastoral counselor and my first audience. He helped me tell the truth even when it was very uncomfortable; and he taught me how, when two people truly connect, the ground between them is always holy.

On Not Having Breasts

I WAS surprised that I did not cry about losing my left breast. I cried about having cancer. I cried about x-rays and body scans. But I didn't cry about not having two breasts anymore. Breasts don't regenerate, I told myself. It's not going to come back. You're not going to get another one. The one I had left looked exceptionally nice to me, but I didn't really grieve for the other. Why not? Did I want to talk about it? asked my friend Jeff from the church who was helping me. "Sure," I said, but I didn't have much to say. We concluded that he sure would miss a testicle if he were in my shoes, but we didn't resolve the problem of my unmourned breast.

Later it hit me. Of course! As an adolescent I'd shed as many tears as it's possible to shed for not having breasts. Buckets. Bathtubs full. Whole hecatombs of tears. I would lock myself in the bathroom and ignore the pleas of four younger siblings while I cursed God. My first feminist act: cursing God for slighting my womanhood. He might as well have made me a boy, I raged, turning racks of towels sodden. He might as well not have made me at all. What an insult. I might as well not have any, as be mocked by such pathetic, Lilliputian excuses for breasts. (I was a very well-read adolescent.) Where was my mother? you may ask. Surely a mother could soothe those tears. My mother had her hands full nurturing four younger children—one of whom was always smacking its lips at her perfectly delicious breasts.

What about the inverse proportion argument—you know, less breast, more brain. Who are we kidding? Brains are not as good as breasts, as every American knows perfectly well. Besides, breasts are for boys; you can't have one without the other. And what's a girl without a boy? In 1959, nothin', that's what. Maybe things are different today.

Well, what about padded bras or stuffing them with things—handkerchiefs or socks? Uh-uh. I knew perfectly well that would be only a temporary stay against disaster. This is the scenario as I imagined it:

He takes me to a movie. He puts his arm around me. I snuggle up to him (knowing that this is asking for trouble). He snuggles. We snuggle. It is very nice. On the screen the moment of truth impends. His hand falls casually on my breast. I pretend I don't notice. I snuggle some more. This is awfully nice. His hand begins to caress my breast—"breast," as if it's something just discovered. A miracle, perhaps? But my heart is heavy. When will he find out the truth? He reaches under my blouse. I am frozen with fear. He moves his hand confidently up under my bra and squeezes my...socks, "SOCKS!" he bellows. SHE'S GOT SOCKS IN HER BRA! WHAT A GYP! WELL. THAT'S ENOUGH FOR ME!" And, in my scenario, he stalks out of the movie in disgust. Someone—usually a stunning blonde with stupendous breasts (real ones)—silently hands me the discarded sock. A tube sock, I believe it is. All eyes are upon me as I rush tearfully and full of shame out of the movie theater. Duly punished. For false advertising.

No, socks weren't the answer. So there was nothing to do but cry. Until there were no more tears to cry about breasts. No wonder I didn't cry when the left one was cut off. I already knew about life—at least where breasts were concerned.

On Being Told
You Have Cancer for Sure

TWO of my grandparents died of cancer. And my uncle. My
father-in-law too. My cat Woodstock succumbed to cancer a
month before mine was diagnosed. Cancer surrounded me. I
took every "cancer profile" test I came across—never missed a
pap smear, never let a dentist x-ray my mouth, avoided air travel.
Here are some of the things I never ate (except on alternate
Shrove Tuesdays and Leap Year): bacon, hot dogs, ham, corned
beef, pastrami, Mississippi catfish, soft drinks, coffee, whole milk,
liver, unpeeled fruits and vegetables (unless they came from my
own *organic garden*), anything fried—especially deep-fat fried. I
ate meat maybe four times a week, had one drink a day—at
most—and scrutinized every box, bottle, or can for ingredients of
more than three syllables. Smoke? NEVER! Microwave? Are you
kidding? I took vitamins—organic, of course. I ate yoghurt
(unflavored) and lots of fiber. Occasionally I hired Wanda to use
the poisonous products we Americans must have on hand to
ensure the cleanliness of our homes. The staff at the Pet Palace
risked *their* lives de-fleaing my pets. I always used fly swatters,
never insecticides in spray cans.

Boy, was I keeping myself safe from cancer. I never made
myself a nuisance about it. Hardly ever. If there's one thing worse
than getting cancer, it's getting a reputation for being a weirdo.
Like almost everyone else, I'd rather die than be a weirdo. So I
did eat the odd hot dog and doughnut and fast-food burger.

My surgeon was a very sweet man. "I'm afraid the news is not
good," he had to tell me after my biopsy. I could tell he *really*

didn't like having no good news for me. I'm sure he wanted to say, "I was right! It's not cancer at all. Go in peace." That's what I had imagined such a nice man saying. I'd made him do a messy biopsy under a local anesthetic, without any Valium—for either of us. So it wouldn't be cricket for him to have to come out and say, "You've got cancer."

Well, guess what? The sweetest of surgeons finds cancer. And it's probably a good thing! It's probably a damn good thing. But I could tell he didn't like it one bit all the same. I certainly didn't care much for it either, as you can imagine.

"Well, what do you recommend?" I inquired.

"A mastectomy tomorrow," he replied, still not liking it. "Shall I find you a hospital bed?"

"Yes," I said.

Well, you win some, you lose some. But wait a minute. What about dread? Or at least the "it's not fair just think of all that stuff I haven't been eating and how good I've been and the fly swatters"? Why wasn't I panicking like everyone else? My doctor confessed he'd slipped me some Valium after all. Could a terror of cancer as gargantuan as mine be masked by a few drops of Valium? Even mainlined? I was sure it couldn't. Maybe I was just numbed by the horror of it all. I'd surely freak out later like any normal cancer victim. I ordered liver for lunch and ate it, all of it. I drank a cup of coffee. What the hell.

My friend Jeff from church came to the hospital. "What are they going to do to you?" he asked.

"Cut off my left breast," I replied.

And then I cried. Not for the breast. From relief, spelled c-o-n-c-r-e-t-e. No more walking on eggshells wondering if the cake would fall. The cake, clearly, had fallen. Now I would eat my liver and drink my coffee and figure out what to do next. Maybe run down a new recipe for cake.

4

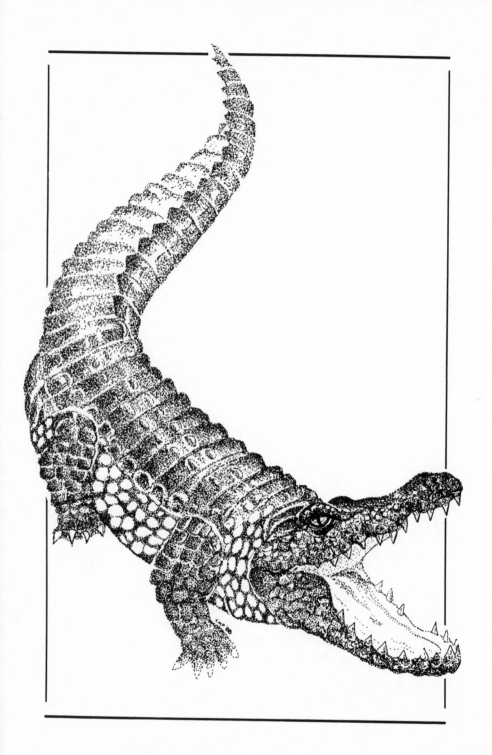

A Lot on the Book of Job
and a Little on Cancer

ONE of the things many people do when they get sick is decide to read some in the Bible. Reading the Bible is one thing they always meant to do more of, but never quite got to, much. And when you're good and sick and wondering "why?" the *Book of Job* kind of seems the natural place to start. That's what I did, anyway. Here's what I found.

A narrator in *Job* sets the stage. Job's from Uz. A good man—I mean really good—"perfect and upright," says the Bible. And he had tremendous respect for God and "eschewed evil." That means if he got the merest taste of evil, he gagged and spit it right out again. If anyone deserved God's blessing, seems like it was Job.

He was blessed with fertility—seven sons and three daughters (not *too* many daughters, we notice). He was blessed also with material goods: 7,000 sheep, 3,000 camels, 600 yoke of oxen, 500 she-asses, and "a very great household" (plenty of wives, concubines, servants, and slaves). He had everything that could make a man happy—or so you'd think. And everyone did: they witnessed all this blessedness and knew that Job was "the greatest of all the men in the East."

"In the East." Some learned commentator doubtlessly will inform me that "in the East" is a synecdoche for "the whole world." Maybe so. I like to think, though, that even back in Job's day, without the wonders of science and the evening news, most fairly alert people knew that, in addition to the East, there was a

West and a North and a South. So what? Well, I think, if we are alert, we may gather from this phrase that Job is in for a mighty big surprise: namely, that there are more things in the world than he has dreamed of. Like boils. And dust heaps, to name a couple.

Why doesn't Job know? The narrator doesn't make this clear, but he drops a hint or two. Job's sons spend a lot of time in their houses...feasting...with their three sisters. Hmmm. Job doesn't have time to find out about boils and dust heaps—not to mention all the rest encompassed by North, South, and West. No. He is afraid that his sons are sinning. (So is the narrator, apparently.) Job worries, "It may be that my sons have sinned and cursed God in their hearts." Incest was not all that uncommon in the Old Testament—though God didn't like it one bit. (It's not all that uncommon today, either, and God probably doesn't like it any better now than He did then—for very good reasons.)

Poor Job. What's a father to do? (I know what my father would do, but that's probably neither here nor there.) He does the best he can: he offers up burnt offerings for them. He does this, the Bible tells us, *continually*. That's why he doesn't know about the other points of the compass.

Meanwhile, as Job is trying not only to be good himself but for his children as well, Satan is intrigued by all this frantic goodness. He takes it up with God, the authority on goodness. "Job seems to think of himself as the proof of your pudding, Lord," says Satan. "Why don't we taste him a bit?" Satan probably suspects that a father with so many screwy sons must have a weak spot somewhere. "Okay," says the Lord. "Just don't kill him."

"Okay"—and that's the end for the sons, the sheep, camels, oxen, and the whole household.

"What kind of God is this?" you may well be asking. Be patient—you're getting ahead of the story.

Is Job still good? "How can I be good with nothing left to burn?" Job might have asked. Maybe that's where Satan got the idea of the blisters and ashes. But maybe not; Satan is never at a loss for ideas himself.

Poor Job. Here he sits, his skin covered with blisters and boils and nothing under him but a heap of dust (or ashes, depending on your translation). Not only that. Everyone can clearly see that he doesn't deserve God's blessing anymore. Especially his three friends Eliphaz, Bildad, and Zophar. They come to comfort him—and, boy, are they shocked. They take one look, and can't talk for seven days, they feel that bad about it all. Poor Job, they think, what has he done to deserve this? Poor Job. Are they ever glad *they* don't deserve such a fate!

After seven days of this comfort Job speaks up. "Damn," he says. "I wish I'd never been born." He suggests a number of fairly unimaginative ways this might have been made to come about if he'd been arranging things: stillbirth, maternal rejection, infanticide. If God didn't mean to bless him, He could easily have arranged for one of these things to happen, Job reasons. "Isn't it rather nasty of God to give me a taste of happiness and then pull the rug out from under me? Isn't that rather sadistic of the Lord?"

His friend Eliphaz is shocked to hear the Lord spoken of in this way. He himself would never *think* of speaking so unfairly about the Lord. "Can I say something, Job?" he asks. "I'm sure the Lord wouldn't consider doing this to you unless you deserved it somehow. Think now," says Eliphaz. "Who that was innocent ever perished?" (Which tells us that Eliphaz didn't know much about the North, South, or West, either.) "I only point this out to you for your own good," closes Eliphaz. The jerk.

"Bullfeathers," replies Job (I'm loosely paraphrasing). "What kind of comfort is this? Here I am covered with dirt and worms, and every time a blister heals another one pops out. Show me how I deserve this."

"Cool it, Job," then answers Job's friend Bildad. "God doesn't pervert justice. You must not have made enough burnt offerings for your children's transgressions. Remind God—nicely, mind you—that He's supposed to be just and forgive our weakness, and I'm sure He'll make it all up to you. In my experience He always evens up the score if you wait long enough." (Which tells us that Bildad, too, lacks knowledge of North, South, and West.)

"That's what I always thought, too," answers Job. You can tell he's pretty upset and confused about the way things have turned out. "Just let me die in peace," says Job.

9

But here comes Zophar, friend number three. "Someone's got to talk sense into this man," says Zophar. And we can easily guess who it's going to be. Does Zophar know about North, South, and West? Nope. The righteous are rewarded and the wicked are punished in Zophar's corner of the world too.

Perhaps we may speculate that Eliphaz, Bildad, and Zophar are upset with Job because his misery threatens to open up their cozy eastern corner to the North, South, and West. It is clear in the next chapters that they certainly do not like to hear the sort of thing Job is saying. Maybe life's not so simple after all, Job suggests. Maybe God's not all that easy to get a handle on. Can we imagine that Eliphaz, Bildad, and Zophar are thinking, Maybe this could happen to us too! They criticize Job's tone of voice, his flashing eyes, and they compare his words to the wind (the east wind, of course!).

Job does not take all this comfort lying down. He continues to tell it to God as he sees it. And hey! Look! Seems like somewhere he's learned about the North, South, and West! Or maybe it took a boil or two to bring them to his attention. Anyway, now he knows about the poor and hungry and naked, about barren, childless women. He knows about Ethiopia! But he's sure he's never done anyone much harm and he's sure all of this must be a *big* mistake.

Elihu speaks up. Wait a minute. You always hear about the *three* comforters of Job. Who is this Elihu? Elihu turns out to be the biggest turkey of all. He hasn't said anything up to this point, he declares, in deference to his elders, but now he's just about had it up to here with their impotence and Job's insubordination. He, Elihu, knows how to call a spade a spade! God is good; Job clearly is not or he wouldn't be suffering like this. It is an abomination against God to suggest that a good God would allow an innocent man to suffer.

Elihu, we note, also hasn't got around much—but boy does he know a lot about the Lord! "Listen to me, all of you," he says, "and I'll clear it up for you: Blah blah blah God. Blah blah blah great. Blah blah blah Job. Blah blah blah sinner."

Out of the whirlwind (a wind that gets around a great deal in the Bible) speaks the Lord to Job. "Who is this turkey?" asks the Lord, referring to Elihu. "Sin's got nothing to do with it. What it's

10

got to do with is: I am the Lord and you are a human being."
(Again I paraphrase loosely.) Then God goes on a bit for several
pages saying some beautiful and scary things.

Job seems to feel better. God, we notice, fails to tell him
about His little bet with Satan. Being the Lord, of course, He
doesn't have to. We also notice that God knows *a lot* about not
only the East, but also about North, South, and West. He knows
about everything from the hawk to the hippopotamus. God
reminds Job, for instance, of the crocodile:

No one is so fierce that he dares to stir him up....

Who can strip off his outer garment?

Who can penetrate his double coat of mail?

Who can open the doors of his face?

Round about his teeth is terror.... His sneezings flash forth
light, and his eyes are like the eyelids of the dawn.

Out of his mouth go flaming torches; sparks of fire leap
forth....

His heart is hard as a stone, hard as the nether millstone.

When he raises himself the mighty are afraid; at the crashing
they are beside themselves....

He counts iron as straw, and bronze as rotten wood....

He makes the deep boil like a pot; he makes the sea like a
pot of ointment....

Upon earth there is not his like, a creature without fear.

Isn't that terrific? You can tell God really likes that crocodile.
The *Book of Job* is full of beautiful and scary stuff like this.
Everyone should read it for themselves.

Job doesn't have too much to say after hearing the bit about
the crocodile. Now he understands the difference between himself
and God. I'll bet he's glad to know crocodile-taming's not up to
him! I'll bet he's glad God likes him just being a person. God is
pleased that Job understands sin has nothing to do with
it—although He does leave Job sitting on his ash heap a bit
longer.

11

God seldom hurries, though, I've noticed. What kind of God *is* this that Job's got? Well at least the kind you can talk to.

God gives the Comforters their comeuppance (except for Elihu who seems to have faded into the woodwork—who can blame him?); God promises to forgive their comfortings if Job asks Him to. Job does, and lo, it's like awakening from a bad dream. Here come Job's brothers and sisters to comfort him. They bring him money and jewelry and God restores his former fortunes. In fact he's twice as rich now as before: 14,000 sheep, 6,000 camels, 1,000 yoke of oxen, and 1,000 she-asses. Wow!

What about the sons and daughters? Here they come too: seven sons and three fair daughters—and nothing about Job thinking they might be sinning and spending all his time making burnt offerings for them. No. Job knows now that God cares more about hawks and hippopotami and human beings than He cares about sin and burnt offerings. What's sin to a crocodile-tamer? Job is to gird up his loins and be a man and leave the redeeming of sin—even incest—to God. Isn't *that* good news! Seriously. It seems to work for Job. "After this," says the narrator, "Job lived one hundred forty years, and saw his sons' sons, four generations. And Job died, an old man, and full of days."

The *Book of Job* turns out to be a pretty complicated business. In fact, according to Bible scholars, it's a mess in lots of ways. But it is full of beautiful and scary things, as I've said, and I like it a lot. It's a good book to read when you have cancer.

I'm not nearly so polite to God anymore. He seems to prefer human beings and crocodiles to turkeys. In fact, I'm not nearly so polite to anybody, including doctors. Connecting, I've decided, is what's important. Politeness, it seems, is often a good way to avoid really worthwhile encounters with others. If you doubt this, review how Job's friends operated.

So sickness has made me a little more feisty. And it's kind of fun—being feisty, that is. One of these days maybe my sneezings will flash forth light too. I don't expect to wake up some morning with a new breast. But sometimes I check the meadow behind my house for a sheep, a camel, a yoke of oxen, or a she-ass or two.

On Roller Coasters

WHEN you are told that you have or may have cancer, you immediately feel as if you've lost control. All your plans go flying out the window—not neatly through an open window to be done with. No, right through the pane, leaving you crumpled among the shards. I was just beginning to feel comfortable and in charge after a difficult divorce. In one afternoon I regressed two years—completely overwhelmed by how much was left undone, how many loose ends were lying around—not the least of which was an eight-year-old son. Time, it seemed, had run out. Why hadn't I...? Why couldn't I have...? Fear of death, to my surprise, didn't enter in much. Attachment to life was too strong a habit to consider death in any more than an intellectual or practical sense.

What frightened me was the sense of being flung suddenly on a roller coaster, you know—hurtling along who knows where for who knows how long, never knowing when you might plunge or climb precipitously at breakneck speed, only to drop into bottomless space. I've always hated roller coasters. I like to know who's in charge, that the equipment to which I entrust myself is in good repair, where exactly the ups and downs are. And, if at all possible, I like to see who's in the driver's seat. (You can imagine how much I like flying!) I wonder, now, how much I really liked life. I certainly liked being in control.

When my friend Jeff called on me in the hospital the day before my mastectomy, I thought I had control of my feelings, if nothing else. I thought I was doing pretty well, considering I'd just come from a biopsy which wasn't supposed to be malignant (at least according to the most recent diagnosis), and was only a few hours away from the removal of a breast.

13

"How are you?" asked Jeff.

"Fine," I said.

"What are they going to do to you?" he inquired.

"Cut off my left breast," I whispered, as my roller coaster slid over the top of the incline and careened downwards with a force that threatened to deprive me of all human dignity. I sat on the hospital bed swallowing tears and trying to feel strong. I didn't know Jeff that well and thought he just might bolt for the door if he knew he was ministering to a terror-stricken zombie who just happened to look like an ordinary sick person. If I'd been in his shoes, I'm sure that would have been *my* inclination.

When you feel like a terror-stricken zombie, though, you'll take almost any chance—even the chance of telling the truth to someone you hardly know. "The worst part of all of this is feeling like you're on a roller coaster," I snuffled, not, for the moment, valuing human dignity very highly.

"You're going to be on this roller coaster for quite a while," he told me, not bolting.

He knew about roller coasters! I stopped swallowing the tears and we both sat there feeling the wind blow through our stomachs. It wasn't fun, but it wasn't as bad as before. "Quite a while" is better than "forever." I'd found someone who knew about roller coasters. Maybe he knew about the North, South, and West too.

The Cat in the Clothes Dryer

WHEN I was in the hospital after my breast was removed, the nurses took very good care of me. I could tell they felt bad that I had cancer. They asked about my pain and watered all my flowers. It was not easy to cheer them up. They'd seen what cancer could do.

They wished their patients had all rushed to their doctors immediately with their lumps and thicknesses, their bleeding, their changes in bowel habits, headaches, nagging pains. "Doctor," the nurses wished their patients had said, "will you have a look at this breast? It doesn't seem quite normal this month." Or, "Doctor, I just can't seem to account for this diarrhea I've been having."

Instead, here they were. Sick. And scared. Wishing they'd seen their doctors sooner. People tend to avoid the truth, though. I've noticed that when people think of truth, they often think of it as "the awful truth." Maybe this is why women don't do breast examinations and don't get pap smears. This is not good, because it makes it all the more likely that "the awful truth" will prove to *be* awful.

No one wants to face "the awful truth," of course. I look at it this way: if there is an "awful truth," it's a matter of facing it now or some other time. You can choose. It's like the night I thought I'd shut my cat in the clothes dryer.

I'd come home after midnight, paid the baby sitter, taken a bath, finished my biofeedback exercise, and snuggled into bed when it hit me: I hadn't seen the cat since I came home. He was a young, vigorous cat—not the sort who would be curled up asleep somewhere. He was the sort that hid around corners and pounced out at you, the sort that followed you about and wanted to sit on your book or lap whenever you sat down. Where could he be? Where *could* he be? Then I remembered. Before I left the house four or five hours ago, with the cat threading itself in and out between my ankles, I'd hurriedly transferred a load of clothes from the washer to the dryer, slammed the door, and started it up.

And now I was snuggled in bed, cozy and warm, very tired, and thinking, Oh my God. What if the cat jumped into the clothes dryer and I didn't notice and I started it up with the cat inside? Being an English teacher, I thought of Wordsworth's departed Lucy, "rolled around in earth's diurnal course." And I thought of the pet hamster that got loose on my residence hall floor when I was a college student. It got loose in October. We didn't find it until November when they turned the heat on and the hamster carcass began to roast, caught between the radiator and the wall. For a while no one wanted to think about truth, though it smelled truly awful. Everyone emptied her wastebasket, I remember, hoping that the truth was only an old egg, or maybe a piece of fish sneaked out of the cafeteria for consumption later. No fish, of course, in Bloomington, Indiana, was worth sneaking out. No, by evening everyone had to search in earnest. The awful truth was faced, and the poor rodent finally fished out from behind the radiator. With a coat hanger. In grisly, sizzling pieces.

I lay there for a long while, thinking about the cat. Thinking what a nice cat it was. How much my little boy loved it. How a cat would feel rolled round in a dryer with towels and blue jeans and jockey shorts. What a cat might do, a cat that had just been fed a big dinner, finding itself in such a situation. I did not want to find out. I wanted to go to sleep and wake up to discover that it was all a bad dream. If it wasn't, though, I was going to open that clothes dryer in the morning and find a dead cat. And I was pretty sure that a dead cat left overnight in a clothes dryer would not have improved with age. The question was: would I rather find a dead cat tonight or in the morning? All things considered, I thought if there was a dead cat to be found, I'd best find it tonight, although I surely did not want to find it at all.

The cat, as it turned out, was not suppurating in the clothes dryer after all. He had eaten his own dinner, half the dog's dinner, and had sunken into a torporous sleep. When he opened his big yellow eyes, stretched, and bounded up the stairs, I was very pleased.

I went back to bed and dreamed of one of my nurses, the one who was trying not to face "the awful truth."

"When did you notice something was wrong?" she'd asked me. I told her.

Was it a lump? How fast did it grow? Did it hurt? When did I go to the doctor? She was small and pretty and had red hair.

"Do you think you might have a problem?" I asked her.

"Yes," she said.

Had she seen her doctor? No, she hadn't had the time; she had a family and worked. Doctors' offices were closed by the time her shift was over.

"Listen," I told her. "It's better to find out early. I lost a breast and twenty-two lymph nodes. You don't have to."

"I don't have time to be sick," she said.

I thought about that as I watched her change my dressing. "Is that comfortable?" she asked.

"Listen," I said. "You're a good nurse. I'd like to think of you going on being a good nurse. Go see your doctor." She said well maybe she would, putting the finishing touch on my bandage.

I saw her once more before I left the hospital. "Made a doctor's appointment yet?" I asked. She hadn't. She didn't look like she would, either. I hope she did.

The Inner Guide

BECAUSE my doctor and his nurse both forgot to tell me about Compazine, I discovered my inner guide. Compazine is a mild but effective drug well known to chemotherapy patients. If you are going to feel like throwing up, Compazine can make you feel less inclined that way. An inner guide? That's the person inside you who always tells you the truth. The Simonton team, working with cancer patients in Texas, discovered that many of their patients had such a person to consult. Sometimes this person took the form of a wise old man or woman. Sometimes the guide was a cartoon-like character. Always, though, he or she told the truth.

The evening after my first day of treatment, I started to read the Simontons' chapter on inner guides. I was dubious. All I need is one more inner voice, I thought to myself. Grumpily. Cancer patients probably get into this fix in the first place because of too many voices. I had the "good girl" voice: "Look at how good I'm being," it clamored. "I don't lose my temper; I'm sweet and understanding; I eat all my peas." Then there was the voice that told me what to do if I wanted to get ahead: "Get to know the right people; work harder; be professional." I had a competent mother voice: "You'd better spend more time with your child, be more patient, discipline him correctly, or he'll turn out to be a mess." Then I had the laid-back, sophisticated-person voice: "Look relaxed, smile, make a clever allusion, don't say anything dumb, laugh," it reminded me. And of course I had a feminist voice: "Don't let them walk all over you; speak up; are you going to stand for that?" Like children crowding around a Good Humor man, these voices competed for my attention.

21

No. I really didn't need any more guides, I decided, laying the book aside and drifting off to sleep. The next morning, though, I awoke and, without benefit of Compazine, I did not feel good at all. There did not seem to be too many positive thoughts to think. One treatment down, four more to go this week, and I was already feeling lousy. Opening my eyes or moving would make it even more real, so I just lay there. "Shoot," I thought, or something like that. "What am I going to do now?" None of my voices seemed to be feeling all that well themselves. None of them spoke up, anyway. So there was a great deal of quietness around me for a change. I just continued to lie there. Then I remembered the chapter I'd read the night before. "Why not?" I thought.

"Do I have an inner guide?" I called out in my mind to whatever or whoever might be in there.

"Yes, I'm here," said someone.

"Who are you?" I asked, not quite believing this was happening.

"Your guardian angel," said the voice.

"I thought guardian angels were for children," I grumped to myself, still not really believing all of this.

"They are," replied the voice.

"What's your name?" I asked, changing the subject.

"Carl," said the voice promptly.

"Carl!" I snarled inhospitably. Why not something lovely like Veronica?...or Cecelia? I thought. But no, on top of everything else, I'm going to be stuck with a male guide. Named Carl. Jesus Christ, who ever heard of a guardian angel named Carl? "I never liked the name 'Carl,' " I told him. "I hope you at least spell it with a 'K,' " I said, thinking that "Carl" with a "K" was classier.

"No. A 'C,' " said Carl.

Tired by these unexpected epiphanies—at 7 A.M. before breakfast, feeling sick and all, I gave in to what appeared to be the inevitable.

"Okay, Carl," I said. "Why don't I feel good? What do you think I should do?"

"You're hungry," he answered. "Get up and eat. Then go for a walk."

Could it really be as simple as that? I'd always supposed that anything worthwhile had to be complicated. And difficult. That morning, though, simple solutions seemed best.

I did not enjoy eating breakfast, but I felt better afterwards. A lot better. I did enjoy my walk. Afterwards, as I rubbed my feet with skin oil (I did this after my bath every day, wanting my body to know how much I liked having it around), I apologized to Carl for my inhospitality. "How long have you been with me?" I inquired.

"From the beginning," he said.

"How come you never spoke to me before?" I wondered.

"You never asked me anything that you really wanted an answer to."

"You won't go away, will you?"

"Listen, we're in this together," he said.

That afternoon I told Jeff about Carl spelled with a "C." Worried about how he was going to receive this news. I knew how most people would receive it!

"You know what 'Carl' means, don't you?" he asked. "It means 'ordinary person.' "

I should have remembered, me with my Harvard Ph.D. in English. On the other hand, that was the "me" who always felt different—super-responsible, super-sensitive, super-capable, and also super-afraid not to be super. That "me" would probably be the least likely to discover I shared quarters with an ordinary person!

Using Mental Imagery

IN their book *Getting Well Again*, the Drs. Simonton relate how they have their cancer patients practice mental imagery to help their bodies heal. They point out that if we can make ourselves sick by negative thoughts and expectations, we can use the same power to help us get well again. You need medicine too, but medicine alone doesn't work as well as medicine plus positive mental imagery.

The first couple days I did mental imagery exercises, I used a Pac-Man scenario. I pictured my white cells as endless rows of Pac-Men gobbling up all the threatening bits and creatures they came across. It was kind of fun, but I was aware of an underlying uneasiness. Why? Aha, of course! I've never been any good at all at video games. My eight-year-old son always beats me. So does my friend JoAnn who used to get irritated at me for being so bad. If you're seriously trying to win a game of life or death, I decided, better not clutter it up with old business like feeling incompetent.

So I re-imagined my cancer cells as greyish, gelatinous masses. Gravy-flavored. My neighbors, the Pettersons, had a wonderfully energetic German shorthaired pointer pup named Snoot that lapped up everything. I'd seen her flatten children as old as eleven with one boisterous, bouncing leap and so thoroughly lap up their faces I was always surprised there was any face left. So I recast my immune system as long-eared, pink-tongued pointer pups. During my daily imagery exercises, I imagined them cavorting through all the systems of my body, ears flying, enthusiastic pink tongues lapping up gravy-flavored gelatin. I pictured packs and packs of these puppies sniffing out gravy-cells and running them to the ground. The gravy-cells never had a chance.

After about three weeks of unleashing my pointer pups, a bunch of dazzling-white street-cleaning machines appeared on the scene. They had very bristly, round brushes and were extraordinarily efficient at sweeping up any gravy-cell detritus and escorting it through my kidneys, bladder, and colon. In another couple of weeks, I discovered that a rampage of unicorns had added themselves to the scene. They ran with the pointer pups and delighted in stirring apart the gelatinous masses with horns or hooves, making it easier for the pointer pups to get their tongues around them. In another couple of weeks, I found schools of sleek, hungry-mouthed diaphanous fishes, busily capturing loose gravy-cells that had drifted into the blood stream, somehow having escaped the pointers and the street-cleaning machines.

I expect as the weeks and months pass, I will find additional beneficent creatures patrolling my blood stream, marrow, bones, and organs. What I find marvelous and wonderful is that most of them came forward and presented themselves for this work on their own. Except for the pointer pups, I did not say to myself, "Well now, I wonder what kind of mental image I could see to knock off cancer today?" Instead, they came unsummoned from some mysterious and vasty deep. Even the pointer pups appeared in a flash with minimal intellectual effort on my part. As soon as I realized that Pac-Man might not be the best idea and began paging through my image bank, out sprang good old Snoot, complete with pink tongue, rambunctious paws, alive with energy and high spirits.

Most of my image-creatures, I notice, are living, not mechanical things. The appearance of the street-cleaning machines was a real surprise. But I suppose in a culture as machine-oriented as ours, it would be more surprising *not* to find the mechanical enlisted in a health matter. (Spend some time in nuclear medicine these days and you'll know what I mean.) My fleet of street cleaners have become humanized to some extent— the way C3PO is humanized. They take their work very seriously. Sometimes I climb into one, in my imagination, and lead the fleet's cleanup activities. It's kind of fun to sit up high and pull

26

the levers that manipulate the brushes, raising and lowering them, making them turn, and driving the machine forward.

The relative nonviolence of my image creatures also came as a surprise to me. I could have had Dobermans, barracudas, and tanks. I'd like to think this is because I'm such a pleasant, peaceable person. But I remember all too well how I automatically bashed my assailant in the subway. And I don't like to admit it, but I have probably mentally garroted, machine-gunned, or submerged until drowned about as many troublesome people as most persons. No, I'm not essentially any less inclined to violent solutions than other people. What I think is that we're all part of one ecosystem, these cancer cells and I. They can't stay because eventually they might destroy the system. But I can't see myself becoming more healthy by encouraging parts of me to rip into other parts of me.

"Hey, these cancer cells have gone berserk," you may say. "They're threatening your life. Why not add a barracuda or a tank—just for good measure?"

The way I see it, though, cancer cells are bad enough without barracudas. Or tanks. And so far the chemotherapy and my pointer pups seem to have things under control.

On Losing Your Hair

I WASN'T a bit pleased about losing my hair. I wasn't expecting
to lose it. Doctors, nurses, and hairdressers all assured me that
I'd be okay in that respect—probably. "As long as you don't
expect to look like Crystal Gayle, you'll probably not have a
problem," said my first oncologist, Dr. Gordon.

Learning to live on a roller coaster, dealing with a mysterious
and frightening drug interaction and a newly-discovered death
wish kept me from fretting about something as remote as losing
hair. Until I combed my hair one morning and found a good
handful of it in my brush. The next time I washed my hair, the
bottom of the bathtub looked as if I'd bathed two large, molting
German shepherds there. As I cleaned out the tub, I felt a
confusion of emotions, particularly fear and guilt. I pushed them
aside, concentrating on solving the drug interaction crisis, but
they clamored for attention whenever I combed or washed my
hair. Finally, I had to admit that I was upset—more upset about
losing hair than about my breast. When I looked at all that hair
in the bathtub, I got weak in the knees, whereas I could gaze
with relative equanimity at my now single-breasted front. I could
admire its differentness. I could even imagine that there were
nice, interesting men in the world who might also admire
something a bit out of the ordinary when it came to breasts.

But watching my hair come out in batches was another
matter! Why? A bunch of possibilities came to mind. There was
vanity—a woman's crowning glory being her hair and all. Most of
my personal vanity was attached to my legs, though. They always
did what I wanted them to and always looked nice, while my hair
had always been unruly and a disappointment to me.

29

Well then, what about the Cultural Significance of Hair in Western Tradition? (When you have a Ph.D. you always try solving problems this way. Sometimes it works, sometimes not.) "My brother is a hairy man," says the jealous Jacob of his brother Esau in *Genesis*. Then there's Sampson, both in the Bible, proleptically, and later in Milton. Jesus, who assures us in the New Testament that God's knowledge of us extends to knowing the number of hairs on each of our heads, found very pleasing the luxuriant locks of the Magdalen, I recalled.

What about virility and sexuality, associations not to be dismissed lightly? And health and maturity? Infants and the senescent in their second childhood are bald. And there are hair shirts and hair-raising stories, hairy situations, letting your hair down—and getting things out of it, making your hair stand on end, a hair's difference, being missed by a hair, and the hair of the dog that bit you. These associations and expressions all suggest the importance our culture attaches to power, sin, fear, and other strong emotions, measuring, and recovering from hangovers. Did these account for my response to the hairy bathtub and brush? No doubt in part, but I still didn't think that was the whole truth of the matter.

Finally, I went to Carl. "What the hell is going on?" I asked. "All this hair scares the bejeezus out of me—and why should I feel like I've just been caught in the act of adultery in Macy's front window when I wipe the hair out of my own bathtub?"

"Remember," said Carl, "you've just come down off a thirty-seven Dilantin level. That's enough to make everything seem worse. And then there's that well-meaning person who told you the other day that after your hair came out, ninety-nine percent for sure you'd stop menstruating ('experience the change of life' I believe were her words) and that you'd have uncontrollable hot flashes. Give me Eliphaz, Bildad, and Zophar any day—and throw in Elihu for good measure." That helped some.

I wrote to my friend Jeff. "Hair's a very personal thing," he wrote back. "I like mine a lot and sure would hate losing it." That helped too. At least one other rational person could understand what seemed on the surface an excessive reaction to the temporary loss of hair. But were these feelings excessive?

30

I turned once more to Carl. "No," he replied. "You're thinking of nuclear war. You know, they drop the bombs, you start throwing up, your hair falls out, and you die."

"But this is chemotherapy—not radiation," I protested. "And I've always avoided those TV end-of-the-world specials."

"You grew up in a city ringed with missile sites; you read *On the Beach* and *Canticle for Leibowicz*. What do you think of when you hear 'Waltzing Matilda'?"

"Not billabongs," I admitted. Discovering my subconscious associations between hair loss and death banished the fear.

But there was still the guilt. "Why guilt?" asked my mother. I'm not sure, but I think it has to do with harboring a secret and protecting others from it: namely, that you might die—and that they might too.

Every day people said how great I looked and how they knew I could lick this thing. I always heartily agreed—never feeling very comfortable about it. The truth about my rapidly thinning hair seemed to give the lie to the image of myself as leader in a pitched battle against a dangerous disease. Daily, hourly, I assented to this image although I knew that frontal attack was just not my style. I had once beaten off an assault in a New York subway by wielding an umbrella with a force and viciousness that surprised me. But, like most women, I ordinarily wasn't good at head-on attack. I continued, however, to say, yes, of course I was going to win, get the best of this thing, come out on top. Then I'd go home, shut the bathroom door, and comb my hair out. I would look in the mirror and see a liar.

Everyone wants living proof that cancer can be vanquished. It didn't take much to realize that this wasn't only my battle but the battle everyone fears they, too, may have to fight. Who could let them down? Yet how could I honestly accept this fearsome role, finding not only in my heart but in my hairbrush daily reminders of vulnerability and mortality? I had every intention of getting well and trusted my body to repair itself, with some help from medicine and reasonable cooperation from God. Look how well I'd come out of surgery. Three days in the hospital, lots of yoghurt, and I was practically as good as new. In some ways better. I suspected, though, that when people said, "Cancer can be whipped," they didn't want to hear about my yoghurt. I don't think they wanted to hear about the more contemplative lifestyle I was adopting, either. Cancer is something, according to opinion, that you have to get before it gets you. Sort of like Communism. You'd better drag out all your ammunition, rattle it loudly, and prepare to launch an all-out attack with everything you've got. Never mind that this may lead to vomiting, loss of hair, and death.

The way I see it, all-out attacks, in some cases, are not the appropriate course of action. A personal attack on the subway when it's you or him and when you can see him is one thing. When the threat is from within, or from foreigners incompletely understood, with whom you nonetheless share an environment, the guns-ablazing approach is less than satisfactory. All my doctors assured me that they could do in those cancer cells with no problem, such cells being, contrary to popular opinion, weak and confused. Enough radiation, enough chemotherapy, enough surgery—no problem. But enough would do me in, too. Better to be as nonintrusive as possible, encouraging the body to put its house in order, than go in with all you've got.

So I take my treatments, meditate, eat yoghurt, and enjoy my Crystal Gayle wig. My friend Jeff wrote, "I'm not a doctor, but I think you are going to be healed." And when I clean the hairs out of the bathtub, I hum "Amazing Grace" more often than "Waltzing Matilda."

Being Nice to Your Body

THE latest thing in cancer treatment is not new drugs. They're still pretty much at the dynamite stage in cancer treatment. It'll probably be a while before they reach the ICBM stage—and another while before they find a way of seeking out and zapping cancer cells without wiping out bunches of all the other kinds. Currently a lot of good cells bite the dust along with the bad ones. Causing a variety of natural reactions including vomiting, loss of hair, premature menopause, itching, loss of appetite, and on and on. It's good to be very nice to your body while all this is happening. Poor thing doesn't know what hit it. Here are some ways I found to be nice to my body.

I gave it a hot bath or shower twice a day and talked to it afterwards, anointing it with skin lotion. I would say things like, "Thanks for carrying me around all day, legs. You're looking as good as ever." Or, "You can relax now, arms. We're going to bed in a while." I was especially nice to those parts of my chest and underarm where nerves had been cut and now felt semi-dead. "Wake up a little bit," I'd say. "I like you just as much now as before," rubbing in a little extra lotion.

I gave my body regular exercise. The Simontons say that their patients who exercised an hour three times a week did better than those who didn't. I don't like exercising much, but I started walking briskly around the hospital two days after my surgery. I could almost hear my body say, "Hey, I'm alive! I seem to be making it!" After I left the hospital, I walked a mile or two every day. Three months after surgery I enrolled in a fitness program. I'm still not real fond of exercise, but I persist. It's one of those things, like crying, that I always feel better after.

Crying's something else I've come to indulge in. My friend Josephine who is a counselor tells me that suppressed tears are like poison. "You wouldn't drink poison, would you? Well, don't swallow your tears," she said. I don't like crying any better than exercise, but I have to admit it's better to cry for five minutes than feel like wanting to all day.

My body likes being fed good food so I'm careful these days to choose healthy things to eat. I don't make a big deal of it, but given a choice between a hot dog and chicken, I usually choose chicken. I eat lots of plain yoghurt and take vitamins, although some of my doctors say women's magazines overrate their benefits. (I'm constantly amused at doctors' needs to criticize women's magazines.) My doctors also marveled that I was ready to leave the hospital three days after surgery and at how quickly my incision healed!

Relaxation is something else most bodies thrive on. My friend Jeff suggested I learn biofeedback. I now use it three times a day: before breakfast, after lunch, and before going to bed. It seems to drain off accumulated tension and stress. I get a lot less crabby in late afternoon and early evening than I used to. My son, though he was at first jealous of my quiet times, now recognizes their value. "You sure are grumpy," he'll observe. "Why don't you do another relaxing?"

Finally, there's laughing and hugs. Laughing, as Norman Cousins points out, is actually a form of exercise. A good laugh exercises your insides, reminding them how nice it is to be alive. Even the beginning of a smile, medical journals report (and women's magazines too), releases chemicals in your brain that aid in the healing process.

And hugs? Nothing's more important to a body than hugs. Before I got cancer I was shy about hugs. "What does this hug mean?" I'd wonder. "Will this person want more than a hug?" "Will that person find out how I really feel about him (or her)?" The answer to both those questions, I know now, is yes. Because what a hug means is life reaching out to life. Sometimes that's scary. Choosing life is scary. But it's a lot better than the alternative. A lot.

Internal Conflict and Cancer

UNRESOLVABLE conflict, especially when you keep it all inside, does not help you get well again, say the Simontons. So when I realized that my friend Jeff knew about roller coasters, I told him I was pretty upset about where my life was going. Who was I supposed to be? What was I supposed to do? I felt like an adolescent again. It was embarrassing.

When I was an adolescent I thought God might want me to be a priest. In those days God didn't want women to be anything except good wives and mothers. I studied church history and Greek, just in case, but mostly I worried a lot. I was very timid. Most priests I knew were a warm, outgoing, good-humored sort. They laughed a lot. I didn't laugh. I hardly ever smiled. I'd better be an English teacher, I decided. Especially after I heard a group of priests laughing together about a woman who had asked about women being priests. "I told her it wasn't a theological matter, at all," said one man. "My dear, it's a matter of our not wanting you!" They all laughed.

Well, that just about settled that. With my crummy breasts and all, I wanted to be wanted more than anything else. So when I received a B in Greek, I heaved a sigh of relief, feeling certain that was a sign from God. I didn't have a feminist guide until much later. She would surely have set me straight on the word of God. "Damn men," I believe she might have put it. "Where do you think you got a God like that?"

But back then, the only God I had gave women B's in Greek and crummy breasts. Wanting to be wanted more than anything else, I headed into English, got all A's, a Ph.D. from Harvard, a husband, child, job, and a nice house. All this time I was very good. Then I got a divorce and breast cancer. Was one crummy breast better than two I wondered? Somewhere along the line I'd learned about laughing.

Had I wasted my life? That question tormented me more than the thought of death. Suddenly, having chosen a life work because it was easy and because I couldn't smile seemed pretty cowardly. I hated having been a coward. "I'm just not satisfied being an English teacher," I told Jeff. "Maybe it's not what God wants me to do."

"I have a priest friend," said Jeff, "who worried a lot about what God wanted him to do. Then he received, simultaneously, a call to two similarly attractive parishes. He went into the church, as he knew he should, knelt before the altar, and consulted the Lord. 'Lord,' he prayed, 'which church would you have me serve?' He waited expectantly. And, for the first time, God spoke to him from the altar: 'George, I really don't care,' came the response. 'Just stay in touch.' "

Getting cancer was not all bad. With it, I also got Jeff and Carl and a lot of growing up. I got a Crystal Gayle wig and lots of hugs. I got a long vacation. I got to know my mother better. I got new ideas, time to read and write. I got to like myself better. And I got a better God. Actually, I think it was the same old God I'd stuck with even when I thought He'd short-changed me on breasts and A's in Greek. I forgave Him that, and He forgave me for thinking that I had to take on the whole male establishment of the Episcopal church to please Him. Like Job, I learned that God is not a sadist. Sometimes, though, it takes some sitting on an ash heap to find that out. Job sat on the ash heap of his life— making continual sacrifice for sins—without knowing it was an ash heap. The Lord gave Job a bona fide ash heap—so he could see what an ash heap his life was, compared to all that was out there. To his credit, Job rose to the occasion, wanting, I think, to break out of his cozy corner, but not knowing how. Or maybe he was a coward too, until he had nothing to lose—until his life was no longer crowded with worries about sons and daughters and wives and concubines, not to mention the hundreds of oxen and the thousands of camels.

Jeff believes that the Lord comes along to each of us looking for a place to be born. When we say with our busy, conscious minds, "But there's no room in the inn," He doesn't go away. No. He goes underground. To the cave of the subconscious mind. And He waits there for some room to open up. Sometimes, as I said, it seems to take an ash heap. In some cases, boils, or cancer.

Who was I supposed to be? What was I supposed to do? I don't know. I do know that one way or another, my life is involved with feeding sheep—currently they are the lambs I shepherd through my freshman composition or Shakespeare class, or protect from the various wolvish forces which abound on college campuses these days. I had a dream recently. It came up out of the cave of my subconscious to be born and bring me peace. In it, I stood in a grassy spot surrounded by a countless number of people—a "fair field of folk," in the language of my favorite medieval dream vision. They were all pressing towards me. I knew they wanted something of me, but I felt confused and helpless. How could I 'feed' this mob? What was I to give them? Jesus at least had something to work with, I thought in the dream. Not much, but there was a loaf of bread, and the two small fishes. What did I have? Then, miraculously, my cancerous breast which had been removed, regenerated. Out of it suddenly poured streams of milk which was gratefully received in the open mouths of the multitude who stood quietly, taking in what they needed. It was a healing dream—a dream to be shared. But when I went to talk to Jeff, I could not bring myself to tell him these things. The roaring laughter of those priests from my childhood still rang in my ears.

"Don't worry about it. Jeff will understand," said Carl. "I'm sure he knows about original sin."

"I know," I said. "But it makes me sad."

Oncologists

MY first oncologist (cancer specialist), like my surgeon, was a very sweet man. He was short. Somehow that's reassuring when you've suffered chronic smallness of breast. I liked his eyes too. They were large and blue. They were eyes that had looked truth in the face a long time ago (maybe the truth about being short). They weren't kind eyes. I was glad about that. When you have cancer, you don't like kind eyes. What you want are eyes that say, "I'm glad to be alive and I'm really glad you are." Eyes that say, "I'm sorry you are sick, but I wonder, besides that, what kind of person you are." Eyes that say, "Let's work on this problem together."

Kind eyes say, "You poor thing. How will you survive this?" They say, "I'm sorry you're sick—boy am I glad I'm not." They say, "Put yourself in my hands. You can't possibly do anything for yourself." They say, "I'll suffer with you to the end," which, along with the rest, is a lot of rubbish.

Eyes are much more important in an oncologist than height. Not lying is the other quality you want to look for; it is a rare commodity. My oncologist probably got a D in med school in "How to Lie, I and II." In Lying I they teach a jocular, breezy bedside manner that communicates, "You're doing very nicely." They also teach how not to invite or encourage unpleasant questions—especially the Biggie: "Am I going to die?" or "How bad is it really, Doctor?" If you do well enough on breeze and jocularity, no civilized human being—even most sick ones (that's how well-civilized we are!)—is going to bring something as gauche as rampant metastasis or death into the conversation.

Doctors, consider now. Have you ever had a patient who said, "Doctor, I want to discuss this rampant metastasis with you"? Or, "About this death that you say is coming to me...." No. But in case a patient should edge close to such statements, in Lying I you learn to take the initiative in the question category: "Well, how are we today? Good! You look very well. Having any discomfort? Eating okay? Moving your bowels? Good! Good! Any questions? Good! Tonight we'll do some x-rays, tomorrow maybe a little CAT scan. The nurse will tell you about that. Are you going to die? Ho-ho-ho. Aren't we all! There now. I'll be around to see you tomorrow."

That was Lying I. In Lying II, you do role-playing. You are taught more sophisticated prevarication than the "aren't we all?" routine. In Lying II, it is always emphasized that breeziness and jocularity, done well, usually eliminate the need for prevarication. Here are some variations of the "ho-ho-ho aren't we all?" model, just in case:

1. "There's every chance, if there is no recurrence in five years, you will be considered cured." (Only a very liberated woman of the most obnoxious kind will ask about the chances of surviving the next five.)

2. "Now let's not start with the pessimism," or its corollary, "Let's think on the positive side"—followed by a discussion of appetite and bowel movements.

3. "You'd be surprised what science can do these days!"

4. "Wouldn't I tell you?"

5. "We'd better talk to the Man upstairs about that." (And that doesn't mean the radiologist or the surgeon.)

6. "Believe me, I've treated patients in a lot worse condition."

Scrutinizing the patient's chart, then looking up in a vacant way as if the question has not been heard and turning the conversation to the patient's bowel habits is also considered highly effective.

"Why all this prevarication?" you may ask. Well, doctors are human too. I should know; my father is one—and a very nice one too. No one likes to look someone squarely in the face and tell them the whole truth—especially if it's not good news. I should know that too. I'm a college professor. When a student says to me, "Is there any way I can pass this course now?" do I say, "Are you kidding?" or, "Not a chance," or "I'm afraid not," or even, "Based on your record I think it unlikely." No. Who am I to rule out a miracle? Anything's possible, they say. So I tend to say something like, "If you work hard, we'll see."

Doctors and college professors prefer to be Mr./Ms. Nice Guys just like anyone else. What doctor wants to look a patient in the face and say, "Yes, you are going to die and probably soon." Who can blame him/her? Besides, not all patients who ask about dying care all that much for truth. Why do they ask, then? Well, for one thing, patients often want their doctors to think well of them— especially if their doctors are tall. "Give it to me straight from the shoulder, Doc," they say, but here is what they mean: "This is a rotten business. Please tell me something to make me feel better."

Personally, I didn't ask my oncologist the Question. Why? Didn't I want my doctor to think well of me? I cannot prevaricate: I did. Did I perhaps not want to cause him social pain? That was part of it. But there was something else too: I really wanted to find out for myself.

My doctor, doubtless, got a D in Lying I, as I said before. I know he didn't fail it because he *did* volunteer the "five years and a good chance of cure" routine. I didn't mind. He was, as I mentioned, a sweet man with truthful eyes. His eyes said, "Listen, your guess is as good as mine, but I do want you to make it. Let's try."

41

Change of Life

THREE days after my surgery, feeling pretty sore, I began
packing to leave the hospital. It was, I remember, a Sunday
morning. To my astonishmemt, I began to menstruate. Right on
schedule. Lower back pain, cramps, and all. Ordinarily, I did not
hail this event with any pleasure. It hurt; it was messy; it
interfered with my routine. My mother had called it the curse and
that was pretty much how I usually thought of it. My friend Kate
and I, before we finally got pregnant, used to joke about having
twin hysterectomies to rid ourselves of this gratuitous nuisance.
Jan, however, my apartment-mate in graduate school who threw
up from pain when she had her "period," referred to this monthly
ordeal as "my friend"—to my absolute amazement. Until the day
I left the hospital and realized that despite the repeated shocks of
a cancer diagnosis, a biopsy under a local, the removal of a
breast, and a no-holds-barred talk with my oncologist, my body
continued to do its usual thing.

Four weeks later, despite a drug interaction with my first
series of treatments, it happened again. Same pain, same mess—
but now I saw it as a sign of life going on, a reassurance that my
body was working right, of its resilience.

So when I got the word, from someone trying to be helpful,
that ninety-nine percent of those on my chemo recipe "experience
the change of life," I was not too happy. Suddenly I realized that I
did not want to lose this new-found friend. I tried to think
positively: no more cramps; I wouldn't have to buy tampons or
Tylenol anymore; there'd be one less thing to complicate my
agenda; I wouldn't have to fear pregnancy at the age of forty-

one. My friends don't call me "Pollyanna" for nothing. I have a gift for finding a bright side. I'm like the child who, finding a pile of horse dung under the Christmas tree, called for a shovel because "surely there has to be a pony in here somewhere!"

My pony-faith failed me in this instance, though. I hung up the phone, went to my room, and cried. Loudly. For a long time. Then I wrote to Jeff. "I'm afraid I'll die after all," I wrote. "This woman says I'll ninety-nine-percent-for-sure experience the change of life" (I was so upset I couldn't remember the word "menopause") "and something in me says 'why not just let go?' " I told him about my hair falling out too. It was not a very cheery letter.

"Don't hide your dying from me," Jeff wrote back, "if you think that's happening." It was good to know there was someone I didn't have to shovel out ponies for.

When my next menstrual period came due, I didn't even bother to buy tampons or Tylenol. I just lay low and waited for the hot flashes. My body surprised me again—and I remembered the roller coaster.

I was reading Thomas Merton and this is one of the things he said:

"Conversion...is not merely the conversion from bad habits to good habits, but *nova creatura*...."

Being created anew. And this thought came to me, without my digging: the experience of having cancer is turning me into a new creature. I have chosen to exchange the ways of death for a new life and have felt the stirrings of a new creature within me, myself newly conceived. The stopping of menstruation, in this context, seems no more threatening than it did when I became pregnant with my son.

Am I still pony-hunting? Perhaps. Or perhaps it's that *nova creatura* I have been so constantly stirred to seek. The restlessness and turmoil I've felt since my second treatment—as I anticipated "the change of life"—has been, perhaps, the excitement of feeling you're only one or two more shovelsful away from what you're digging for.

Sharing

COUNSELORS and clergymen have been selling us on sharing
for some time now. It's good, they've been telling us, to share.
They recommend sharing our feelings, concerns, concepts, joys,
sorrows, anger, fears. I think the hippies started all this talk about
sharing. They thought we should share showers. And beds too. I
don't know how counselors and clergy feel about shower-sharing.
I think they probably hedge on beds. At least the clergy do.
Usually.

   Until I got cancer I never tried to work out why all this
sharing talk made me uncomfortable, why it gave me about the
same feeling as Jesus talk. I felt guilty about this lack of charity in
myself, but no amount of trying would banish the urge to growl
or regurgitate whenever I heard someone suggest that "we all
share together." One year, enough people offered to "share their
thoughts," or "share their ideas," their feelings, concerns, and
concepts that my front left incisor had to be recapped because of
being set on edge so often.

   When I found myself in the hospital with cancer, however, I
began to share like crazy. I couldn't help it. In fact I had the
feeling that if I didn't, I'd be in even bigger trouble. I felt stuffed
up with unshared things: fears for my young son if I should die,
anger with a friend, discouragement at what seemed a waste of
my life, embarrassment at some truly foolish choices,
disappointment with myself, an unbearable sense of weariness. It
was bad enough having your left breast and armpit stuffed with
cancer. You can imagine how being stuffed up with all those
other things felt. The doctors took charge of the breast and

armpit. Seemed like it was up to me to take care of the other stuff. And I did. I opened my mouth and, you might say, regurgitated. It wasn't fun; it was embarrassing. It hurt—more, I think, than the surgery. Physical pain never did make me cry. Telling Jeff about all the other stuff made me cry every time. I hated it. "Every time I talk to you, you make me cry," I charged. Actually I know now that it wasn't his fault.

What happens, I've figured out, is something like this: Everyone has what you might call "cry creatures" inside. The job of cry creatures is to make sure that not too much stuff like anger, fear, weariness, or disappointment builds up inside a person. Whenever cry creatures begin to feel a bit crowded, they begin to shove on the built-up stuff. Any sensible person will start talking right away when they feel that shoving. They'll say something like, "Boy am I ever feeling upset with you," or "I feel like crawling into a hole and pulling it in after me," or "I sure wish I hadn't made such a fool of myself." If you say things like this right away, the cry creatures smile at each other and curl up together in your now-more-spacious insides and go to sleep. And you feel much nicer.

If you aren't sensible or ignore the shoving or don't feel it, the cry creatures have to shove real hard. They shove all that stuff right up every hollow space they can find. Some of the spaces aren't all that big, so the shoving hurts—especially if some of that anger or disappointment gets caught crosswise.

Anger and disappointment, I've found, hurt the worst coming out. Maybe because they know they're not all that attractive. They try to stay inside where no one can see them. Have you ever seen those capybaras they have in zoos? They look rather like tailless beavers with claws but appear to weigh about one hundred and fifty pounds. Well, that's how anger and disappointment feel trying *not* to come out. How do the cry creatures get them out? Well, they couldn't do it by themselves, I'll tell you. What they do is this: they wait until the stuffed-up person meets up with someone who knows about anger and disappointment and fear and who pays attention to his or her own cry creatures. Someone who knows that crying is something you feel good after. This person's cry creatures will call out— "Hey, you got a stuffed-up person over there?"

"Sure do," will come the reply.

"Need some help?"

"You bet! We've been shoving for months and nothing gives."

"Okay, let's get to work. Start shoving."

The stuffed-up person begins to feel that heavy pulling, hurting feeling in his or her chest. He or she knows what you have to do to make it go away for a while.

You can tell a joke. If it's funny enough, you can make everyone laugh until they cry. Or you can complain about the way things are being run: "I wish the provost (or president or boss or staff or pastor) would get the simple facts through his (or her) fat head and straighten out this mess." Or you can throw around a lot of threats. This is the favorite of persons stuffed up with fear: "If they don't stop this nonsense, I'll go straight to the dean (or boss, or bishop)."

The cry creatures keep shoving, though, and they mean business. It doesn't feel good being stuffed up like that. The other person's cry creatures start shoving too. This person will recognize the feeling and know it's not a joking matter. So he or she will say something like "That's a pretty funny joke, but, you know, I'm feeling kind of sad inside. Don't really know why. You ever feel that way?"

Usually that's all it takes. You take a breath, start to talk, and all the stuff you've been stuffed up with pushes up your chest into your neck. Some of it gets caught crosswise around your Adam's apple. The rest pushes its way up your throat into your sinuses. It's either cry or burst open. Most people cry. Then they talk.

Do they share? No. I've changed my mind about that. It's fairly easy to share—sharing being a fifty-fifty proposition: I give you some of mine and sometime you give me some of yours. Sharing often masquerades as giving. I think that's what makes me uneasy about sharing-talk. Sharing's fairly safe—fifty percent being all that is risked. Sharing only rearranges and redistributes the stuff in stuffed-up persons.

What I did in the hospital when I got cancer was not share. What I did was give. I didn't "share" my anger with Jeff. I gave it

49

to him. I didn't "share" my disappointment, fear, weariness. I gave them to him—ugly, misshapen, weak creatures though they were. Not the sort of things you ordinarily think of as gifts. Not the sort of things you ordinarily want to accept as gifts. But when that's all a person has to give at the moment and he or she gives them to you, you take them. Because they are rare and wonderful—a treasure. Only giving unstuffs; only accepting changes stuff to treasure.

Checkups

I HATED going for my six-week checkups. The day of my appointment my congeniality rating was probably about as low as it could be. I'd sit in the waiting room with all the other cancer patients waiting my turn to be checked. About twenty dollars worth of checking it usually was. I listened to the friendly voice of Dr. Veeder laughing and joking with his nurses and patients. "You'd think we were all here for an office party or something," I'd find myself growling. "Here we all are, stuffed with cancer, and we're supposed to laugh?" Then I'd think how unreasonable I was being. What was wrong with me, I'd wonder. What did I want, anyway? Fear and trembling? Gnashing of teeth? Blood, sweat, and tears? Sharing? Certainly not sharing.

Dr. Veeder, like my first oncologist, was short—a good sign. But I suspected he'd done better in Lying I than Dr. Gordon. Not that he ever actually failed to tell me the truth when I asked him; I believe he always did, and I appreciated that.

I'd go to my checkups with my list of questions and observations. "I'm having these headaches," I'd tell him. "Not real bad ones. But I never used to have headaches. It worries me." He always listened. He never said I was cancer phobic. He never said that I was worrying too much.

But I never felt as if we were really connecting, either. Well, I'd tell myself, it can't be much fun having so many patients die on you—even less fun if you connect with them. But then I couldn't help thinking that maybe fewer would die if they felt more connected. Dr. Levinson who wrote *Cancer: Its Causes and Prevention* thinks that is true. He thinks cancer gets started up in many people because they feel disconnected. To get well, he says, you have to reconnect—"fuse" is the word he uses. Lots of doctors don't much encourage fusing, though—at least with them.

I'd say to my doctor, "I seem to be on a ten-day menstrual cycle." "This sort of thing is not at all uncommon with people on chemotherapy," he'd say. That was good to know and it made me feel a little better, but I didn't think he really got the picture. When you've got cancer, having a lot of blood coming out of you constantly is scary.

I told my dad, who is a doctor, about my ten-day cycle. "What should I do?" I asked him. "Go out and buy stock in Kimberly-Clark," he suggested. He seemed to get the picture a little better. "My father thinks maybe I should buy stock in Kimberly-Clark," I told my friend Jeanne who was a biologist. She drew me some pictures. "Your body's just getting too many messages too fast. It's trying to do the right thing," she assured me.

As my fourth checkup approached I found that my attitude was as bad as ever. Truculent is the way I'd describe it. I'd get felt over a bit, asked a few questions: "How did your last treatment go?" "Fine," I'd say. "Any nausea?" "No, just a few days of not wanting to eat much." "Good," he'd say. I'd ask about my blood count. "It's about what I'd expect," he'd say. Sometimes I'd be brave enough to ask if it were high or low. Usually it was on the low side, but high enough that I knew my mental imagery exercises were helping.

I never told Dr. Veeder about mental imagery. He'd probably think I was a little strange. "Pointer pups?" he'd probably exclaim. "And street cleaners? Next thing you know there'll be unicorns!" I wouldn't have the heart to tell him that there already *were* unicorns. Once, though, he told me that my blood count was perfectly normal. I was very pleased. I felt pleased all the way home. Then suddenly I wondered if he meant perfectly normal for a cancer patient or perfectly normal for anyone—for a healthy person? I suspected that this might be a paranoid thought.

I knew that sick people often have paranoid thoughts. The morning I was scheduled for neck surgery sixteen years ago a nurse awakened me early. She said I should get up and take a bath. I did not much feel like taking a bath. "Why?" I asked, not very congenially, as I recall. It was, said the nurse, hospital procedure. Sure, I found myself thinking as I lay sulking in the tub. They just don't want the trouble of washing my dead body.

What prompts such deep and largely undeserved suspicion? I don't know for sure. I think feeling terminally alone has something to do with it, though. This just might be the end of me, you find yourself thinking. And suddenly it seems very important to know that "me" better, and for other people to know that "me" too. That way, the end of you doesn't seem quite so terminal. Terminal—the word they use for persons not expected to get better. When you have cancer, you want to get better, as Kurt Vonnegut says, "everywhichway." You want your body to get better, of course. You also want your relationships to get better. You really feel motivated to get all the stuff done you've always wanted to and always thought you probably could do but never really got around to. Other people, though—doctors, friends, family—seem primarily interested in what's happening to your body. They often tend to think of you as someone who might die on them. When people around you treat you as a potentially dead person, it's hard to keep on believing that you're alive. That you can still get better in lots of ways.

Another reason sick people have paranoid thoughts, I think, is this: doctors, friends, and family members who think of you as a potentially dead person don't like thinking of you as potentially dead. So they pretend a lot. They know it's good for cancer patients to have a good attitude, so they pretend like crazy that you're just fine and they're not worried a bit. You know, of course, that this is rubbish, but you start to pretend like crazy too, to help them. It does not make you feel good; it just makes you tired. After I got used to losing my hair and non-stop menstruation, I usually liked being told I looked good. But I sure didn't like pretending like crazy. And I didn't like being thought of as potentially dead one bit.

Asking my doctors questions reminded them I was alive. "Was my blood count normal for someone with cancer or for a healthy person?" I asked my family doctor. "Normal for a healthy person," he told me, looking at my chart. I was glad I asked. I was very anxious to be a healthy person again.

Maybe that's why I hated my six-week checkups. The oncologist might discover something that meant I was potentially dead after all. Maybe he'd find some more cancer had popped up somewhere. One of these days, when I'd go in for a checkup, the doctor'd feel around in my neck or breast or armpit or push on my liver. Suddenly he'd frown. Pause. Feel or push some more. The suspense would be terrible. "More cancer?" I'd ask, trying to sound casual. "Yup," he'd say, walking over to wash his hands. "Thought maybe you were going to get well. Just can't tell with cancer, though," he'd say. "Better get over and have some blood tests and x-rays and CAT scans." I'd button my blouse, slide off the table and down the roller coaster. Dazed. I'd probably feel very sorry for myself. I'd probably cry. I'd probably think about where I wanted to be buried.

"Buried?" Carl would say. "Wait a minute! This is a blood test he's sending you for. Not a lethal injection! Your doctor's name is Veeder, not Nemesis!" He reminded me that you don't go for checkups to find out if you'll live or die. You go for help in managing your cancer.

"Actually," I told Carl, "Dr. Veeder is a pretty nice man and knows as much as anyone about managing cancer. And to be fair, I think he knows about connecting too. The first time I went for a checkup, he said 'You seem in amazingly good spirits after what must have been a pretty awful couple of months.' "

"That sure sounds a lot like connecting to me," said Carl.

"Well, he's noticed I'm not potentially dead," I said.

"Who knows," said Carl. "Maybe after awhile he'll see you're getting better everywhichway.

Choosing Life

BEFORE my left breast was cut off and most of the adjacent lymph nodes were removed, I would bolt from my bed in the morning, wake my son, take his breakfast order, lay his clothes out, nag him to hurry up, feed the dog and cat, fix breakfast, walk the dog, clean up the kitchen, nag at my son to hurry, get myself dressed and made up, chase my son out the door, lock up the dog and cat. And all the while voices inside me said hurry hurry hurry. On Mondays there would be reviewing the week's school lunch menu, writing a check for lunches and making sure it got in the backpack. Tuesdays, add the wastebasket roundup—dragging the week's collection of trash out to the curb. Every day I would check my *Daytimer* for appointments and throw myself at the world in pieces.

Besides teaching in the English department and doing academic advising, I edited a monthly newsletter, was active in the faculty union, served on a variety of committees, tried to settle a difficult divorce, and spend quality time with Andrew, my son. I was learning to be assertive and extroverted, to pay bills and handle household repairs and keep up the yard, car, and my stiff upper lip.

When the old cat died and the new cat infested the house with fleas and I had a falling out with a good friend, what else was there to do but get breast cancer? Any number of sensible things, of course. For a long time, one of my nagging voices had been saying, What's happening to you? Where are you? Who are you, anyway?

A lot of the time I didn't like how I was feeling. A lot of the time I didn't much approve of myself—whoever "myself" was. The voice kept nagging at me. Instead of listening, I nagged at my son. "When are you going to pick up your room?" I'd say to him, filled with despair that I couldn't have a *Better Homes and Gardens* house where everything stayed neatly in its place. "Eat your vegetables or you won't be healthy," I'd warn, pushing my own food around my plate and getting thinner and more tired every day. "Why don't you ever listen to me?" I'd ask, never really listening to myself. "You're going to be late!" I'd yell while the voices inside me warned, Hurry hurry hurry, you're going to miss it, you may be too late. Then those voices would start fighting with others that said if I didn't slow down and start living right I'd be in trouble with God. I sure didn't want to be in trouble with God. But I didn't know what the trouble was, either—and I couldn't quite get a handle on what God wanted. I was keeping busy. I was doing worthwhile and valuable things. Almost everyone liked me. What more could God want?

I wanted an escape hatch. I wanted peace and quiet. I wanted the struggling to stop. When I was pregnant and weighing over 112 pounds for the first time, I wanted to hang my pregnant belly on a hook for an hour and be free of that weighed-down feeling for a while. I had a pretty easy pregnancy and wanted my baby— just as, coming down with cancer, I certainly wanted my life. But in pregnancy and life you sometimes want mutually exclusive things: you want your baby and you also want to continue racing up the stairs like a gazelle; you want to live, but you don't want to take the time to listen to what's going on inside yourself, do what needs to be done, and stop doing whatever is not life-enhancing.

Why not? Probably because it seems easier to keep on doing what you're doing. That seems crazy to me now. I've stopped throwing myself at the world in pieces. I'm learning to be what Anne Morrow Lindbergh called "inwardly attentive." You can find out the most incredible things when you attend better to your innards. One of the things I found out was guilt. People who feel guilty a lot of the time increase their risk of getting cancer, some recent studies suggest. Being inwardly attentive one day I discovered just how much guilt I carried around. I felt guilty everywhichway. I felt guilty if I were late; if I were on time, I'd feel guilty about coming in feeling rushed. I'd feel guilty if I got angry with someone; if I didn't get angry, I'd feel guilty about avoiding conflict or not taking a firm stand. I really seemed to be going out of my way to feel guilty.

Then, being even more attentive, I realized how often I felt guilty about paying bills or answering letters late. If I didn't have anything else to feel guilty about, I could always feel guilty about that. I could keep the house neat, not lose my temper with my child, get all my work done on time, wash and fold the laundry, practice patience all week with my colleagues, not miss an exercise period. Would I feel good? No. I'd feel bad because of having those bills and unanswered letters hanging over my head. Maybe, I thought, I'm afraid to feel good. Maybe all this guilt is just a way of making sure I feel bad.

Why would anyone *want* to feel bad? I don't know except maybe some of us get used to feeling that way. It's gotten to seem the natural way of feeling. Also, you can feel important when you feel bad: you know, everything's a mess and if you don't sort it out, who will? You can feel righteous: everyone's dumping on you but you know what's right and you'll do it even if it means suffering a lot.

When you feel good, on the other hand, things can seem pretty ordinary. Things are in a mess? Well, you set aside time to work on straightening them out or making them better. Then you set aside more time to plan on keeping them straight. People are dumping on you? Not everyone, right? Maybe they had a bad day. Maybe you deserved it. Maybe you should think about why this is happening and try something different next time.

When you feel good, though, where do you put all that energy that's been going into feeling important and right and defensive and upset? This is probably why you go on feeling bad. When you feel good, all that loose energy starts wanting you to think different thoughts. Do different things. Love different people. Feeling good doesn't keep you from feeling scared. But once you start feeling good, you want to keep on feeling that way; so somehow you find the courage for all the differentness.

"You'll probably think I'm crazy or a hopeless masochist," I said to Jeff when he visited me in the hospital the first time. "In some ways, this cancer is a kind of gift," I told him. He listened. "If this hadn't happened to me, I'd probably have gone right on living like I have been until I died." I told him about jumping out of bed, nagging, rushing, throwing myself at the world in pieces. I told him about the old cat dying and the new cat and the fleas. I told him about my divorce and the multiple voices and the busyness. I told him about the monthly newsletter. There was a lot of listening for him to do.

Then he said, "You know, you have just described my life for me. It's scary."

"I don't think you have to get cancer to change your life," I said. We both thought about that for a while. "I sure don't want to lose another friend soon," I told him. Then I told him about wanting peace and quiet, about the struggling. I told him about the escape hatch. "I think part of me was trying to die for a long time," I said.

"Do you think you are dying now?" he asked. I didn't feel that way at all. In fact, I felt better than I'd felt in years. I felt alive. When you decide to choose life, I think your body gets the message.

Was this new life worth a breast and a bunch of lymph nodes? You bet. I don't feel guilty now when I pay a bill late. "Why are you trying to feel bad?" I ask myself. And I pay the bill. Much easier, I've decided, than paying the piper.

The Cost of Cancer

No two ways about it, cancer is expensive. It costs lots and lots of money. Sometimes you find yourself wondering if the reason cancer cures haven't been found is that there's a cancer lobby out there. Here's the scenario as I have imagined it:

Lobbyist: Hello there, Senator. Do you have a minute to talk with me about this cancer cure we hear tell about?

Politician: Sure do. Been wondering about it myself. Is it altogether a good thing?

Lobbyist: Absolutely not!

Politician: Give me a ferinstance.

Lobbyist: For instance—just think how many people around here would be out of jobs if we cured everyone of cancer.

Politician: Supposin' we just gave the cure to some people. That'd make the rest mighty unhappy, I figure.

Lobbyist: Very perspicacious of you, Senator. Better not mess with it at all.

Politician: Seems kinda cold-blooded, I suppose. You have to think of the common good, though.

Lobbyist: Right you are! Put all those smart folk working on cancer cures out of work, you'll have real trouble, I can promise you.

Politician:	That's for sure. Might start working on a cure for ignorance, thickheadedness, irrationality, and prejudice. Teachers' unions might not like that much.
Lobbyist:	Might be bad news for politicians too, if you catch my meaning.
Politician:	Ooooooh. Better keep those smart guys working on cancer.
Lobbyist:	That's how we see it. Thanks for your support, Senator.

As I've said before, when you have cancer, you're prone to paranoid fantasy. There's probably no plot to keep cancer uncured. Just like there's probably no plot to prevent the marketing of unrunnable stockings either. When you run your last pair of stockings right before an important interview, or when you look at your first hospital bill or chemotherapy bill, then it's hard not to be overcome by feelings of prejudice and irrationality. Most people have never ever spent near that much on themselves at one time in their whole lives!

When I saw those bills for the first time I was pretty upset. Sure hope my insurance comes through, I thought; I'll never be able to pay all this. My next thought was how I sure could get myself one nice vacation for that kind of money. How maybe if I'd given myself a vacation—a month in Colorado maybe, or a week in London—I'd maybe not be paying for having cancer. I thought how maybe for that kind of money I could build myself a swimming pool like that radiologist back home had before he moved on—doubtless, I thought, to an even nicer swimming pool somewhere.

Paranoia, guilt, envy, fear—not a very nice bunch of feelings to deal with while you're staring bills in four or five figures in the face, while your body is not in tiptop shape. Especially if you're feeling sick enough to wonder, from time to time, if you're worth a plug nickel, let alone a sum in four or five figures. You get over that as you begin to feel better.

What you don't get over so easily is the panic you feel about where all this money is going to come from. I knew I had pretty decent health insurance, but I knew it wouldn't pay everything. I worried about losing my job. What would happen then? Or what if my health insurance stopped paying? Maybe they'd decide after a while I wasn't worth the price. "That's about enough for her," I imagined them deciding. "This younger person's got a better chance. We'll give it to him instead. No sense throwing good money after bad."

No wonder I hid everything that came from the insurance company in a drawer where I couldn't see it—out of sight, out of mind. Sort of. Because it was never really off my mind; it just hunkered there.

I didn't have a very good system for keeping track of medical bills. If you don't have a system, the amount of correspondence you have with medical business offices and your insurance company increases astronomically. And it's not the sort of correspondence that generally gives you much satisfaction or pleasure. Better bite the bullet, I finally decided. If there's a dead cat to be found, better find it now.

In this case, as in the case of the cat, there was no awful truth to be faced. I organized the bills by date paid (noting whether it was by me or the insurance company so things would be easier at income tax time). When a new bill or insurance statement came in, I handled it immediately. I carried insurance forms, envelopes and stamps in my briefcase to the doctor's office and sent the bill and the forms straight from there. My purse, I'd discovered, seemed to have a bill-specific black hole into which bills disappeared, never to be found again.

As I changed my bill-paying habits, I thought some about all the other habits I'd like to change: the short temper I'd been indulging more often than I liked; the exercises I'd neglected; the time I wasted; a certain tendency to spinelessness I wasn't proud of; a proclivity for self-pity when I was misunderstood. I spent a lot of time feeling bad about how I'd done things.

It was pretty discouraging—all these bad habits. Seemed like I'd just get to work on one and discover five or six more. It was beginning to look like maybe I'd never get to be the person I wanted to be after all; maybe I was stuck with who I was. I didn't feel very good about that.

While all this not feeling very good was going on, Andrew, my eight-year-old son, and I were taking our three-year-old Lhasa to obedience classes. To turn her into a civilized human being, I told my friends. At first it didn't go too well. Priscilla was smart, but, boy, was she stubborn. She liked things fine just the way they were, she would have told you. She was, she might have added, too old to change, being an older-type dog. What did she want with new tricks? She was just your natural, floppy-eared dog, content to eat and sleep, bark, wag her tail now and then, and, as she would probably put it delicately, evacuate her bowels.

I took her out to practice every morning from 6:30 to 7:00. Andrew practiced with her after breakfast and after school. For three weeks her progress was minimal. Andrew and I got very discouraged. Priscilla felt very sorry for herself. You could tell by her drooping ears, pathetic coughs, and gags. You could tell by the way she dragged along, by the way she hesitated and looked confused whenever she was given a command. "Have a heart," her mournful eyes seemed to say. "Can't you see I'll never amount to much?"

Andrew and I persisted, though, and one morning, five weeks into her course, Priscilla seemed to be getting it. That didn't surprise me. I knew she was a smart little beast. What surprised me was that all of a sudden she was really paying attention. Even more surprising, she seemed quite pleased with herself. Instead of lowering her haunches sullenly to the pavement when I told her to sit, she snapped herself into a forty-five-degree angle, cocked her head at me and, I'd almost swear, grinned. Two weeks later, when I was feeling the most discouraged with myself, I looked down at Priscilla trotting along attentively at my heel and thought, For heaven sakes, if a dog can change, surely I can too.

That week I was trying to break the grip spy thrillers had on me and had turned back to Thomas Merton's *Asian Journal*. There I read a story which, as the Quakers say, truly spoke to my condition. A Buddhist monk and his cellarer were preparing to flee from Tibet during the Red Chinese takeover. The cellarer met his abbot at the appointed place with a train of twenty-five yaks, weighed down with every kind of provision. "But we're going to have to cross mountains and swim rivers," the abbot objected. The cellarer, however, insisted that they would need the provisions. So they set out on their journey. They hadn't gone far when a communist patrol spotted the train of twenty-five yaks—a train of twenty-five yaks marching down the road being difficult to conceal. The cellarer was detained and the yaks confiscated. The abbot, who was ahead swimming a river, escaped. Merton comments:

"I think there is a lesson in there somewhere, too. We can ask ourselves if we are planning for the next twenty years to be traveling with a train of yaks. It probably is not going to work."[1]

That, I decided, was the understatement of the year. And in my case, we weren't talking yaks. We were talking woolly mammoths! No wonder I was getting nowhere fast. No, I decided, I did not want to plan on traveling the next twenty years—or even five—with a train of yaks. Or woolly mammoths.

I told my friends Elvy and Charles about the yaks and the mammoths. They were very interested. "What are these yaks of yours?" asked Elvy. I told her about my money worries. "That's a big yak," I told her. "Maybe even a mammoth. Mostly because I never really know how much I have. I get scared whenever I have to spend any. I'm scared to balance my checkbook."

"Ja, that's a mammoth for sure," agreed Elvy who is from Stockholm. "Tell me about some others." I told her about carrying around hurt feelings and anger; about feeling guilty a lot; about dragging out my divorce; about not knowing what I was supposed to do with my life; about being afraid, even if I knew what to do, that I wouldn't be able to go through with it; about how every drawer in my house and office was a mess; about being very shy with men. We agreed with Merton that it probably was not going to work, trying to travel with all those mammoths. Where I wanted to go, there wasn't room for mammoths. Cancer's not the only thing that eats up lives, we decided. Traveling with yaks can be costly too. Not to mention woolly mammoths.

---

[1]Naomi Burton, ed., et al., *Asian Journal* (New York: New Directions, 1968), 329.

Locker Rooms and Bellybuttons

Dᴵᴰ you ever read those comic book stories where the young bride and groom go off on their honeymoon and one or the other, as they face each other in the bridal suite, begins to confess? She (or he), it seems, was in a terrible accident, and, as it turns out, suffered the loss of a hand, which was so skillfully replaced that no one can detect it. Oh, well, says the other. Do you imagine that a little thing like that could affect the deep love I have for you? She (or he) sighs with relief. About to be embraced entirely, she (or he) suffers another pang of conscience. It wasn't just the hand, actually, but the entire arm. And then we (and he or she) learn that it was both arms. And then a leg, then the other leg—and so on until, on the last page, he or she stands revealed to the other a mass of quivering raw flesh, totally repulsive and totally (as the other finally admits) unlovable. That's sort of how I felt the first time I headed for the gym locker room three and a half months after my surgery.

Locker rooms never had been a favorite place of mine. A locker room was the place where, if you were me, you changed into stiff, ugly green tops and shorts and then spent an hour dropping fly balls, being struck out, pounded into the basketball or volleyball court, or swallowing gallons of chlorinated water trying to stay afloat. A locker room was a place where you were required, in close proximity to some twenty-five other sweaty girls, to strip to the "essential vesture of creation"—which in my case, was pretty essential. Not looking in the least like a dimpled Rubens. And imagining that all the other girls my age did. Not, of course, knowing, since I kept my eyes fixed modestly on my own bellybutton. Hoping to avoid the looks of pity or horror which I was sure would be on the faces of all twenty-four others. I was sure none of them were thinking how really *smart* I must be, having such small breasts and all. I've read a lot about penis envy and can honestly say that, as far as I know, I have never suffered the slightest desire to have a penis. But who has written about breast envy? And I'll bet more girls have suffered the latter than the former.

Did I want a better body because glorious bodies are, in themselves, beautiful and wonderful? I don't think so. I think what I wanted was to be like everyone else. Maybe that's why I always looked fixedly at my bellybutton. Even Eve had one, I'd noticed. Though sometimes I wondered if the old masters, noting that our first mother, too, was less than adequate in the breast department, gave her a navel out of pity. Poor Eve. Poor me. But our bellybuttons at least proved our connectedness to the rest of the human race, other evidence to the contary. Think about that the next time you look at your bellybutton.

The Simontons observed in *Getting Well Again* that their cancer patients who exercised regularly benefited from it. Being determined to get well again, I enrolled in a fitness program at the university, agreeing to walk briskly around the gym three days a week. The night before my first walk, as I began to pack my gym bag, the truth began to dawn as truth has a way of doing. Whoever else was in that locker room was going to see that, beyond a doubt, I was not like everyone else. Somehow I did not think they were going to concentrate on my navel. "Ask for a locker close to the shower," advised my friend JoAnn. That would shorten the distance I'd have to parade in my altogether. But I'd still come in looking normal in my wig and padded bra and then have to reveal to all and sundry that actually, underneath it all, I was something of a freak show.

"Jesus still loves you," suggested a friend. "Good for Him," I thought, not much cheered. The trouble with Jesus-talkers was that they always stated the obvious, but did not hear very well the depths of pain they hastened to soothe. Somehow I didn't think Jesus would care much for Jesus talk.

"I know just how you feel," another friend reassured me. I appreciated her impulse to make me feel better. But I felt awful. I didn't think anyone could know just how I felt.

"I'm going to feel like a freak show," I told Carl.

"That bad, huh?" he answered.

"Worse," I told him.

"Tell me about it," he invited.

"Well, I'm going to feel so absolutely...vulnerable," I said. "Everyone will see how ugly I've gotten. They'll think 'Yuk, she must have cancer or something.' "

"And you care what they think?" Carl asked.

"Yes," I admitted. "It's not nice to feel unattractive and undesirable."

"Jesus still loves you," said Carl.

"Not you too," I wailed.

"Well, I still love you," Carl said. "Of course I've always had a sort of taste for freaks."

"Great," I said. "So did Jesus." I was beginning to feel a little better, though.

"Listen," said Carl. "Here's what you can do."

I listened carefully and here's what I did: I bought a shower cap. When I finished my walking, I zipped into the bathroom, pulled off my wig, stuck it under my sweat shirt, pulled on the shower cap, flushed the toilet, and exited to my locker, where I quickly deposited the wig and undressed. Then clutching a towel modestly to my breast, I ducked into the shower and told funny stories while I washed. I paid special attention to my navel. I dressed, still wearing the shower cap until I could return to the bathroom with my wig—concealed under my sweater.

"Well," I whispered to Carl as I emerged, "we carried it off. Thanks."

"How do you feel now?" he asked.

"Like Superwoman," I laughed.

"I love you," he said.

Connecting

BEFORE I actually got cancer, I was very scared of it. If I ever get cancer, I used to think, the most horrible part would be knowing that something inside me was in there relentlessly taking me over. Something large, it would be. Cunning. Ruthless. Omniverous and increasingly omnipresent. Inescapable. Probably male. It would crouch in there sucking the goodness out of me like a weasel sucks eggs. It would get bigger and bigger. I would get smaller and smaller. I would not be able to get away from it. Wherever I went, it would go too. I'd maybe get someone to take me to a movie or out for a ride to help take my mind off things. "Hey, I'm coming too," the cancer-weasel would say. "You can't leave me behind. I'm hooked in good. You're not going to be able to shake me loose. Try, and I'll hook tighter."

Spooky. Once, years before I got cancer, I went to light a gas oven which had been on for about ten minutes. I'd turned it on while I took a second martini to someone in another room. I took a second one in there for me too. When I came back to the kitchen, it was full of gas. I was full of gin. We're going to suffocate, I thought. Better get rid of it fast. Did I turn off the oven, open all the doors and windows and turn on the fan? No. I lit the oven. That's how much good a Harvard degree will do you after a couple of martinis. I'm probably lucky to be around now to get over cancer.

What happened next? Well, the skin on my right arm—the one I was using to light the oven with—got broiled from wrist to elbow. I began to howl and I tried to run away from the agonizing pain eating up my arm. I tried to run out the kitchen door, intent on getting away from that part of myself in pain. The door was latched and in my pain I could not even perform the simple operation of unlatching. I crouched against the door and whimpered until my cries were heard. But when my husband came to help me, I remembered what to do. I remembered about cold water and ice and about not using butter. All the way to the hospital I thought about not being able to unlatch the door and about crouching there, whimpering.

That's how it would be, I used to think, if I ever got cancer. There would be this sort of animal in me, making me do things, consuming my substance. It would be, I thought, something like being pregnant. Except that there wouldn't be enough substance for both the cancer and me. It might take six months or five years to grow to full term. Cancer doesn't follow rules like babies. And with cancer, I thought, you aren't finally delivered of new life. You turn into cancer food. Until the cancer, having devoured you, "at last eats up itself," as Shakespeare puts it in one of his nastier plays.

It was frightening, thinking about cancer. I tried hard not to think about it and I tried very hard not to get it. If I heard that anything caused cancer, I didn't eat it or use it. And I tried to be so full of goodness there wouldn't be any room for cancer. It didn't work. Why? I mentioned this question to Dr. Lefler, thinking it might help us to connect better. "I was pretty surprised that I got breast cancer," I told him. "I did all the things the American Cancer Society said I should do and I didn't do any of the things they said I shouldn't—except for one."

"What was that?" he asked, very professionally.

"I didn't handle stress very well," I said.

He said there were a lot of people around under a lot of stress and most of them didn't get cancer. "I don't want you to think because you kicked your dog when you were a little girl, you got cancer," he said. A good sign, I thought. He cares about my attitude.

"No, I don't think that's what happened," I replied. He looked relieved. "But," I continued—he stood still and sort of squinted at me. "Maybe I got it because I didn't kick the dog."

"What?" he said, at first not understanding. Then he began to smile. Then he laughed out loud, not just a social laugh, a real honest-to-God laugh—the kind of laugh people laugh when they hear something that suddenly makes sense to them. I like to call it an epiphanic laugh.

"Hey, maybe you should have kicked the dog!" he repeated, still laughing. "That's good! Maybe you should have kicked the dog!" He'd been giving me chemotherapy for six months, five days a week every six weeks. Now he seemed to look at me for the first time. We both laughed. We both knew what it was like to want to kick the dog and never do it. He laughed as he hooked up the chemo IV. He was still laughing as he went out the door.

I thought some more about cancer and connecting. I thought about why the cancer-weasel had never materialized in me. I decided it had a lot to do with connecting. When Linda the nurse-practitioner found the lump in my breast, she put her arms around me while I cried. The radiologist sat up on the x-ray table beside me as we looked over the mammograms. The close friends I told before I left town for my surgery hugged me tight. My doctors were all kind. Connecting was not easy for them, but I could tell they were trying. Connecting's not all that easy for me, either, but I screwed up all the courage I had and told Jeff, my mother's pastor but then still a stranger to me, all the pain in my heart. He hugged me too. He didn't seem to care that I wasn't good enough to ward off cancer. No one who cared for me seemed to care all that much about goodness.

"Could it be," I wondered, "that cancer-weasels live on goodness?" My goodness mostly leaked out when they told me I had cancer. So if that's what they eat, there wouldn't have been enough to keep even a skinny one going for long. I wondered if you have to let go of your goodness to connect. I had to talk back to Dr. Lefler and he had to laugh about kicking dogs before there was connecting. I had to tell my friend Jeff a lot of stuff that wasn't good. This is the hard part: I liked them both and naturally wanted them to think well of me—the real me, though, not just the good me. The me that should have kicked the dog was what Dr. Lefler could connect with. I'm not sure about Jeff. I'll have to ask him sometime.

I still, most likely, have cancer cells floating around inside me. Every once in a while some of them probably try to stick themselves to my innards. Sometime they may gum up the works again. But I'll never have a cancer-weasel. I'll never stockpile enough goodness to feed it. I like being connected, I've decided, even if it's not easy.

One evening while I was doing my mental imagery exercises, something out of the ordinary happened. I'd unleashed my pointer pups and sent them off yapping and snapping after cancer cells. I called up a herd of unicorns to stomp apart some cells I thought might be trying to stick together. I whistled for a cloud of white spiders—the most recent of my mental images. They spun webs around cancer cells and then sucked their insides out.

The fleet of street-cleaners had just hustled the debris down towards the liver to be cleansed when I found myself swimming across a lake. Usually when I practice mental imagery I locate myself under an apple tree in my grandfather's yard overlooking the St. Mary's River. But this time it seemed that I awoke in the middle of a lake and swam slowly to shore. I climbed into a canoe that seemed to be awaiting me on the wooded shore and paddled up a creek that fed into the lake. The woods were fragrant with the smell of pine, and birds called back and forth to one another. Where am I going? I wondered. I did not feel compelled on this journey or anxious about it, though. I could stop whenever I wanted, but I wanted to go on. The creek rounded a bend, bringing my canoe to rest on a soft, silty shelf in shallow water. On a little rise of meadow on the edge of the woods was standing a group of dazzling figures. I climbed up the bank and made my way towards them. I seemed to feel them smiling though they were too bright at first to see clearly. There were several of them and they seemed to move as a group, but one figure laughed in welcome and held me close.

The others came and stood near to us. They sometimes shone out in bright colors although the one I stood close to seemed to be pure light. Then I felt myself filled with light too. I felt well again, whole.

"Did you feel good?" asked Carl when I told him about it.

"No. I felt altogether myself," I said.

74

"Was it sad leaving them?" he wanted to know. It wasn't, because I knew I could come back whenever I wanted.

"Don't go thinking this means you should run out connecting with every Tom, Dick, or Harry," Carl warned.

"Don't worry," I laughed. "I've still got too much goodness inside for that."

Cancer and Intimacy

SOME of your friends may be quite surprised to learn that you think about sex when you have cancer. You may be surprised yourself. I sure was. I was intent on getting well everywhichway, but that way was a little more than I thought I was ready for. If you haven't sorted out the difference between sex and intimacy before, though, when you have cancer is a handy time to do it. Lots of people are going to be thinking of you as a potentially dead person for a while. Since necrophiles aren't all that common, this gives you a little breathing space for sorting out. That's what I thought, anyway.

Six weeks after my surgery, I went back to work. I was very glad to see all my friends. They were very glad to see me. We hugged each other. It was nice. I noticed, though, that some of my men friends seemed kind of uneasy. What was going on anyway? Here I was, learning to connect and all, being a little warmer than before maybe, and what happens? These guys are acting like I might proposition them. I just wanted to have fun. I certainly hadn't been thinking about sex.

"Maybe you ought to," said Carl.

"Do you want to have sex with me?" I asked him. The question sort of just popped out.

"No," he said.

"I didn't think so," I replied.

"Why do you ask?" he inquired.

"Just checking," I told him.

77

"I don't recommend taking any surveys just yet," he advised.

"Thanks, Carl," I said, a little condescendingly perhaps. Does he really think I might start going around asking people if they want to have sex with me? I muttered to myself. What does he think I am, anyway?

"Scared," I hear him say. "Hurting. Alone."

"Not bad, though?" I queried.

"Oh, I don't think so," he said. "Have you talked to Jeff about it?"

"Goodness, no," I said. "I couldn't do that."

"That's funny," said Carl. "I thought you could talk to Jeff about anything."

"Almost anything," I said. Stuffily. "See you later."

I got to thinking, then, about that survey. Supposing I did go and take a poll? What would I discover? This is how I imagine it might go:

Me: Hi, Tod. Any chance you'd want to have sex with me?

Tod: With someone with cancer? You've got to be kidding. You might ask Henry, though.

Nothing daunted, I'd seek out Henry.

Me: Hi, Henry. Can I ask you a hypothetical question?

Henry: Sure. Fire away.

Me: Well, I was wondering what you'd say if I asked if you'd like to have sex with me. Knowing that I have cancer and all.

Henry: Jeez, I don't know. I wouldn't want to hurt your feelings or anything. But I just don't think I could do it. I mean, it's probably my hangup, but when it comes to sex, some things just seem not to turn you on. You might ask Joe, though.

So I look up Joe. I don't give up easily. I've been a union recruiter.

Me: Joe, Henry says I should ask you how you'd feel about having sex with someone with cancer.

78

Joe: Yuk. But why not ask Brad?

I'd give it one more try.

"Brad," I'd say, "I'm pretty sure I know the answer to this question, but what are your thoughts about having sex with someone with cancer?"

"Oh, about the same as having it with a buzzard. Why?"

"Just checking," I'd reply. Then I'd go back to Carl. "Guess what?" I'd report. "Sex and cancer don't seem to mix."

"Talk to Jeff about it," he'd say. "I'm an angel, remember?"

"I keep forgetting," I'd tell him. He'd look pleased. "But listen. I can't talk to Jeff about this. It might ruin our relationship."

"Fill an angel in," he'd most likely say.

"Well, I feel real close to him. Connected. But sex (I'd hasten to add) has nothing to do with it and..."

"Who're you kidding?" he'd interrupt. "He's one of your really neat men. Nice-looking too. If I were human, I'm sure I'd think of sex. Off and on, you know."

"Jesus, Carl," I'd sputter. "This is disgusting. He's married. And a priest. And..."

"Hold your horses," he'd exclaim. "We're not talking action. We're talking feelings."

"Oh," I'd say, a little abashed. "I guess I'm a little confused. Tell me about these feelings."

"Me?" he might protest. "I'm a pure spirit. What do I know about sex?"

"Well, pretend you're not so pure. Use your imagination a little, for heaven's sake."

"All right, but you'll have to help me."

"Fair enough. Let's leave Jeff out of it, though. He thinks all my epiphanies are great, but this might be a bit much."

"'Fraid he might bolt?"

"Well, I might, if I were in his shoes."

79

"What if he did?"

"I'd feel awful."

"Disconnected?"

"You've got it." We'd think about that for a while. There would be a lot to consider. For example, we might consider what my mother's friend Sue wrote for her incest group's newsletter. She wrote about how we're conditioned in our society from a very young age to view intimacy in terms of sexual contact. She wrote about how hard it is, under these circumstances, to build intimate relationships. "Our society," she wrote, "does not promote trust, confidence, and respect as viable components of intimacy. Instead, intimacy is measured in terms of how long a squirt of perfume can maintain its fragrance or how long a breath mint will last."

"Well," I thought when I read that, "at least *this* woolly mammoth's not just mine." It's nice to feel ordinary sometimes.

I thought, then, about the fire extinguisher I'd been carting around with me all these years. Just in case.

"In case what?" asked Carl.

"In case I had to use it," I told him.

"Ever have to?"

"No. But I like to be safe."

"Isn't it kind of uncomfortable, carrying a fire extinguisher around wherever you go?"

"Sure is—especially since I might not even be able to use it if I had to," I confessed. "I lug the darn thing along and then spend the whole lunch hour or evening wondering if I'll have to use it. Or if I want to use it, or, if I should want to use it, which button to push and which end is up."

"But you've never used it?"

"No. But (I hastened to add) I've always been good."

"Remarkable," Carl said. "And this isn't any little kitchen model fire extinguisher, I take it?"

"No," I admitted. "It's more your industrial-sized jobby. I have to pack it along on a yak—or a woolly mammoth. Depending."

"Well," he said. "I'd like you to do some thinking about cars. Then we'll talk some more."

When your Inner Guide tells you to think about cars, even if you're an English teacher and know zilch about cars (and think you care less), you do it. What's there to think about cars? I thought. Well, here are the twelve most important things about cars I could think of:

1. You can go fast or slow with them.

2. The driver decides.

3. They can be fun to drive or not.

4. The driver decides.

5. You can have accidents with them.

6. Most accidents aren't fatal.

7. You should take good care of them or they'll let you down.

8. They can travel in the company of other cars or on solitary streets and roads, depending on where you want to go.

9. The driver decides.

10. If they travel in traffic, other cars always have to be taken into consideration.

11. Sometimes it's good to use your horn.

12. Use your lights when it gets dark and always give clear signals.

Intimacy in twelve easy lessons. Not bad for an English teacher, I thought. I can straighten out the parallel structure later.

"What do you think?" I asked Carl.

"Not bad. For an English teacher. But you'd better straighten out the parallel structure."

"Look," I told him. "I'm trying to get over cancer. I'm trying to live without yaks and woolly mammoths. And fire extinguishers. I'm trying to connect. To hell with syntax."

"That's the spirit!" encouraged Carl. "This subject has been kind of hard for you, hasn't it?"

"You can say that again," I agreed. "I've walked ten miles and bitten eight people's heads off in the last two days."

"Well, I like riding with you," said Carl.

"Want to go for a spin tomorrow?" I invited.

"Are you asking me for a date?" he teased.

"No. For a befriending," I told him.

Is There Sex after Death?

MY mother is a counselor. She counsels people who are in a lot of pain. For some of them it's the pain of committing incest or having incest committed against them. For some it's the pain of abusing their children or of being abused themselves. In a single day she handles a lot of pain. It must be hard to handle so much pain. How does she do it? I don't know for sure, but I think it has something to do with believing in the difference between cows and people.

My mom feels very sorry for cows. When our family drives across the high plains of Kansas or Colorado or New Mexico, my mother, who does most of the driving, still has time to look out over the fields and contemplate the cows. And she'll say something like, "Gee, I'm sure glad I'm not a cow." One morning she said this six times. Or she'll say, "Just look at the poor things," and we dutifully cast our gaze on yet another bunch of Herefords or Angus or indecipherable mixture of brown or black or white or spotted bovine, scattered from highway to horizon. "Wouldn't it be awful to be a cow," she'll say.

"Sure would," we assent, contemplating in our turn the apparent meaninglessness of life for a cow, a range cow who has to spend much of every waking moment finding food, chewing it. Rechewing it. No protection against the weather but the same basically unimproved hides God gave Adam and Eve way back when. Not a whole lot of protection against gusting winds, sleet, snow up to your neck. Not much good against the blazing sun. No good at all against lightning. And no one—except my mother and perhaps God—caring that the end of all this pain is so you can become someone's taco or meatball or liver and onions. Someone who will probably excrete most of the good protein you've toiled to create. All that goodness that is you—has been you—in one end, out the other, and on to the sewage disposal plant.

"Sure glad I'm not a cow," sighs my mom, sure that there is a difference between people and cows.

How can she be so sure? I thought, the summer I was sick with cancer. You get the courage to ask questions like that when you've caught on that it's not asking questions that makes people sick. That it's more often *not* asking them that sickens us.

I was thinking of those people my mother counseled. Those people who, like the cows, had got to be someone's taco or meatball or liver and onions. I thought how so many of us let ourselves be someone else's beefsteak. Or, like pharoah's bony cows in the Bible, we breakfast on each other. I wasn't sure, for a while, that people were all that different from cows.

I knew that since my cancer was diagnosed—and for some time before—there'd been plenty of times I'd felt a lot like a cow. Just dumbly putting up with whatever life dealt out, hoping for the best, hoping that on the other side of the fence the grass might be greener. On the outside, I pretended to be a person. I was very busy. I tried to be good. I tried to make sure everyone knew what a good person I was and what a lot I could contribute, given half a chance. But inside, I felt like a cow. It was not a very good feeling. I tried to get away from it. I tried being even more busy and competent and good, but that just made me tired. And bored.

I tried pawing the earth and making threatening noises, and generally raising a ruckus. Feeling bullish felt a little better than feeling cowish. But you can act bullish for only so long before you run out of energy and are back to feeling like a cow again.

I had just begun trying to act beautiful and sexy when I got cancer. That pretty much cooked *that* attempt to escape the cow in me. Probably a good thing too. When you're being examined medically, it's real easy to feel like a cow. They push and poke and press and peer. You have to hold still for blood tests, body scans. They don't want you to ask too many questions for fear you'll scare yourself the rest of the way to death. They don't want you to tell them you're scared. They don't want you to cry. It's easier on everyone if you're just a cow. I suspected they paid a certain price for cowishness themselves—in not connecting.

I remember the moment I stopped feeling like a cow. It happened when I should have felt most like one. I was alone in my hospital room. My roommate, who had had her gall bladder out while my breast was being removed, was only half conscious and was moaning loudly. Dr. Gordon my oncologist had just left.

He had just explained very carefully how stuffed with cancer my breast and armpit were. How that was not good. How I was too young for this to happen to. I felt pretty grim, as you can imagine. My son was only seven. If I made it five years, he'd be twelve when I died. Beside that, I wasn't finished trying to be beautiful and sexy. Was there going to be sex in heaven? I wondered. Dr. Gordon finished. Did I have any questions? No, I couldn't start chemotherapy immediately. There was some healing to do first. "You've had some real bad luck," he told me. I could tell he didn't approve much of bad luck. He touched my shoulder. "We're going to try to make sure there are no more mistakes," he said. I could tell he was pretty mad about medical mistakes. "Hang in there, okay?" he said. "If the chemo goes well and there are no recurrences in five years, you have a good chance of a cure."

Did chemotherapy cure cowishness? I wondered silently. I felt numb. But I noticed one thing. I noticed that my doctor wasn't feeling sorry for me. He must think we can make it work, I mused.

Cross-legged on my bed, I thought about that after he left. Except for the moaning of my roommate, it was very quiet. My eyes played around the boundaries of my half of the room. There were flowers everywhere on my side. "People don't send flowers to cows," I thought—and smiled as I imagined a cow being presented with a bouquet of carnations or chrysanthemums. Then, suddenly in my bones I knew I was something much more wonderful than a cow. In the very core of my being I knew I wasn't made to be someone's taco or meatball, in one end and out the other and on to the sewage disposal plant.

My roommate began to moan louder. Like a cow. I looked around the curtain to see how she was doing. She looked sort of like a cow. I got up and moved some of my flowers over to her half of the room.

Is there sex after death? (This is the part you waded through all the cows for.) Jeff and I both think so. My friend Rick who also is a priest would probably say no—not without regret, I suspect, but Rick's big on being theologically sound, even if it means a heaven without sex. "There will be no need for sex in heaven," I can hear him saying—with no great enthusiasm, to be sure. Well, in heaven there will be no need of priests, either, but I have every expectation of finding Rick there some time or other. Heaven, if it's worth its salt, must contain all that's good. Not goody good, but really good. So I think Rick will be there and also sex. But only really good sex. How about cows? I don't know. I'll have to ask Rick.

Living on Borrowed Time

"WHEN will you be able to say you don't have cancer anymore?" asked my friend Maurine. I didn't like to have to say "probably never," but thought it was probably the case. That was the bad news. The good news was that for the nine months since my surgery, my immune system seemed to have been doing a bang-up job. From October to August I hadn't had a single cold or flu. Even in the winter months while my son and cat passed strep throat back and forth and students and fellow teachers dropped like flies all around me, I, with a white count that got its socks knocked everywhichway with chemical suppressants, sailed on through. My hypothalamus seemed to be working overtime, really doing itself proud. I credited this to my daily biofeedback and mental imagery exercises, good humor, good food, vitamins, and hugs. In April, my friend Jeanne's cat Jasper sank his fangs up to the gum line in my left wrist—the side hurting for lymph nodes. It did get infected, but a few doses of antibiotic, lots of vitamin C, and I was as good as new.

In June, I vacationed in New Mexico for a week, hiking in the mountains, smelling the flowers. I peered down into craggy canyons at the bottom of which you could always see, if you looked, the cause of all those crags and sheernesses: a slender serpentine stream speeding along to somewhere important, sometimes bearing along its crest rafts in what appeared to be phosphorescent orange flotillas. In July, I volunteered as a counselor at an Episcopal camp for high school kids in central Illinois. It was nice being an ordinary person, doing my share of waterfront and volleyball duty, skit-writing and nightly cabin-checking (making sure we returned with the same number of Episcopalians we came with). No one there knew I had cancer. For a whole week no one asked me how I was feeling. For a week I felt pretty much like everyone else again. I don't know if this ever really happens, but, for that week, it seemed like all cancer stopped dead in its tracks. I felt well again. It was a good feeling.

At the end of the week, my new friends asked would I come back next year? What I wanted to say was, "You bet! Let's plan on it. See you next year." Instead, "God willing and the creek doesn't rise," I told them. "I'd like to!" I said.

Making plans when you have cancer is a tricky business. One way around it is to go back to pretending that you'll live forever— that there'll always be a tomorrow. That the creek'll never rise. Once you've been carried a ways downstream by a risen creek, though, you kind of keep your ear cocked for the sound of rising creeks. Until his dying day, I'll bet a darkening sky gave old Noah a queasy stomach. Despite the rainbow and all, the merest hint of a shower would remind him of the smell of bears and monkeys and big cats, two of each, cooped up together for forty days and nights. I'll bet he kept those ark plans handy.

With an ear for rising creeks and a nose with a memory at least as good as Noah's, pretending, I decided, wasn't going to work for me. What would? "I'm really struggling with the problem of time," I wrote to Jeff. "My current coping mechanism is cleaning out all my drawers and closets," I told him. "At my present rate, I'll need another strategy in about three days."

I waited. Restlessly. A week went by. It seemed like months. I ran out of drawers and closets. I pulled weeds, trimmed the bushes, and had the patio door replaced. I wrote letters and paid bills. I attacked the Augean stable that doubled as utility room and cat haven in my basement. Then I took on the garage, defrosted the freezer, and visited my lawyer. Still no word from Jeff.

To hell with time, I said to myself. I wrote to my new friend Steve on Saturday and invited him to come for a visit. I waited. Sunday was a good day. I anticipated Steve's next letter and his visit. I forgot about Jeff and time. Monday I sort of hoped to find a letter from Steve in the mail. It wasn't there. Oh well, I'd get a letter Tuesday or Wednesday, I thought. Or maybe he'd phone!

From four o'clock on, I began listening for the phone to ring. It rang a lot, but it wasn't Steve. The mail came Tuesday and Wednesday bringing leaflets from Wal-Mart and TG & Y urging me to stock up on back-to-school supplies without delay. Only a bare month remaining. Also an ad for a new brand of toothpaste guaranteed to keep the plaque on my teeth down to a dull roar if used regularly in conjunction with a sound program of dental hygiene.

"I've got cancer, you turkeys," I growled, dumping the mail in the kitchen wastebasket and kicking it all the way through the doorway. The dog and cat cowered satisfyingly in their respective corners. They didn't know I had cancer or was a victim of time. They thought I was the most powerful person on earth. They thought I might just decide to do them in. Feed 'em inch by inch to the garbage disposal, maybe. Or toss 'em into the clothes dryer for a spell. I might've, too, if I hadn't been so busy looking around for a dung hill to sit on. Or some ashes. But Wanda, who does the heavy cleaning, had been there earlier and there wasn't even a dustbunny anywhere. I stomped out into the back yard.

"Carl!" I called. "I need you. Where are you?"

"Out in front by the mailbox, where else?" he answered.

"I'm in no mood for humor," I told him.

"I noticed," he replied. "Want to tell me about it?"

"How do you make plans when you have cancer?"

"That is tough, isn't it?" he said.

"Sure as hell is," I sulked.

"Tell me more," he encouraged.

"I don't know what I've got time to do and what I don't. One day at a time may be okay for some people, but it doesn't work for me."

"You want to know if you're going to die this year or five years from now, or forty."

"Right. I mean, do I eat, drink, and be merry or settle in for the long haul? It's confusing."

"And scary?"

"Yes," I choked.

"Let's think about it," he suggested.

I settled down against the rough trunk of the hedgeapple tree in my back yard and thought. First I thought about Jeff and Steve and how I didn't want to lose them. I thought about how much Andrew my eight-year-old son still needed me to help him grow up. I thought about Maurine. Maurine is my soulmate and fashion advisor. "You've got to buy a black dress this fall," she told me, showing me, for proof, the latest issue of *Mademoiselle*. "I don't know," I'd said. "Black's not my color. Besides, I'd feel like I was dressed to go to my own funeral." She'd winced. "Don't say things like that," she'd said. "Don't remind me that you might die," is what she meant. "I don't want to lose you."

I thought about how I'd maybe like to live somewhere else, how I was feeling penned in after fifteen years in one place. How I might like a new job in a new place—New Mexico, maybe, or Wisconsin, or Massachussetts. But who would hire me—or insure me—knowing I had a life-threatening disease? And that wasn't the worst of it. Who would dare love me?

"Jeff does," said Carl.

"He's a priest; he has to," I said.

"That," said Carl, "was a cheap shot."

"I'm feeling mean," I said.

"No kidding," he remarked, "but tell me about Steve."

"Steve is good," I began. "Not goody good. Really good."

"And does he love you, you think?"

"I think we're connecting—but it takes time and I don't know if I have time. Maybe I shouldn't bother. Maybe it's not fair to Steve."

"Maybe you should just have packed it in on the operating table?"

I thought that over for a while and decided that some time was definitely better than no time. And that I probably wanted to spend it some other way than carving a canyon between my front door and the mailbox. Then the phone rang. It was Jeff. He'd never called before, but I was only partly surprised. I reminded him of my problem with time. I didn't tell him about kicking the wastebasket or wanting to feed the dog and cat to the disposal. I figured AT&T was already rich enough.

I told him about my friend Jeanne who'd just told me she was dying of cancer.

"That's what she said? That she was dying of cancer?" he asked.

"Yes. She just seems to want to hunker down and watch while it gets her," I told him. "But I don't think she really has to start dying now."

"Dying only takes about two days," Jeff said. "Until then, you're living."

"Only two days," I told Carl after Jeff said good-bye. "Until then I've got all the time in the world."

"Time to carve out a canyon?" he inquired.

"I think I'll leave that to rising creeks," I said. "I'm going to get on with my life. And my dreams. Warn me if it starts to feel like rain, though, will you?"

"About two days' warning?"

"How about three. I might want to make a little extra merry."

"Sounds good to me," said Carl. "Three days, then. I wouldn't worry about any creeks rising for a while. Just look at the sun!"

We sat and watched the sky together. All this thinking about time and talking to Jeff had nearly worn me out. The sun was warm. A breath of a breeze stirred the hedgeapple leaves. I'd begun to doze a bit when a thought occurred to me.

"Carl," I said. "Did you get Jeff to call me?"

"No. It was his own idea. He loves you, remember?"

"Uh-huh," I acknowledged, not feeling mean anymore. "Carl," I said, "I'm glad I'm not Noah. I sure would hate to have to start corralling pairs of bears and monkeys and big cats."

"Things do seem to work out, don't they?" Carl said. "Sweet dreams now."

Letting Go

WHEN you're very sick and trying to get well, you want to play it safe. You do not want to have anything to do with anything risky. You don't want new medicine. You want what's tried and true. "If this chemo recipe doesn't work as well as we'd like, we'll try others," Dr. Veeder assured me the first time he saw me. I could see that he was trying to make me feel better, but I didn't want any new treatment. I wanted someone I trusted to say, "Don't worry. You just take this medicine, go to bed for a while, and you'll be just fine soon." "Just hang on for five years and we'll consider you cured," they tell you. So you grab hold and hang on for dear life. You do whatever the doctors say. You try to be very good. This is okay for a while, but as a regular lifestyle, it leaves something to be desired.

Not that I'd ever really enjoyed taking risks. I was a pretty cautious person, actually. I was the sort of driver, for instance, who hated to pass another car unless I could see five miles in all four directions. I bought life insurance instead of stocks. When I went to a party, I checked out what everyone was going to wear so I'd be dressed right. I never burned a bridge. In fact, you could hardly ever get me to cross one. When I came to a river or even a stream, I'd more likely dig in and set up camp, make myself a cozy corner. I stayed in a bad marriage too many years, not only because I thought marriages should be forever, but because facing my mistake was just too scary to want to think about.

When I got cancer, I had, as Ann Landers says, to wake up and smell the coffee. Hardly anything is forever, I discovered.

Hanging on to what's not forever can, I found, get you into hot water just as fast as crossing a bridge. I almost got into hot water with my friend Steve, for example, by trying to hang on.

"I'm coming through town next week," he wrote. "I don't have much time, but let's at least plan on a quick cup of coffee."

"Dear Steven," I responded. "You turkey. If you think I called off a two-year moratorium on men for a cup of coffee, you're a damn fool." I said lots of other things that were pretty foolish too. Including what I considered an adequate reward for calling off my moratorium. Then I hung in there and waited for a letter or a phone call. The dog and cat nearly got fed to the garbage disposal any number of times while I waited. My son got yelled at more than usual and learned some new words and phrases to share with his third-grade friends. One day I said something so nasty to him I called him at school to apologize. "Oh, that's all right, Mom," he said cheerfully—leading me to suspect that he counted the new addition to his vocabulary adequate compensation for maternal ire.

"Dear Anne," Steve finally wrote back. "It was the 'Dear Steven' that got me, lassie. 'Steven' is habitually the precursor of trouble to come. Or a letter of excommunication. Something jolly along that order." A cup of coffee it was to be, but it seemed that no plugs were about to be pulled right away. The cup of coffee, when it came, was actually quite nice. We talked for a while and then said good-bye. "It's funny," I told Carl. "Saying good-bye wasn't even hard. I thought it would be."

"How come?" he inquired. Angels, of course, never have to say good-bye.

"Well, you'd think the more connected you get, the harder it would be to let go."

"Ever done any rappelling?" he asked. "Or rock climbing?"

"You've got to be kidding," I said. "Hanging by a piece of flimsy hemp over God knows what is not my idea of fun."

"Who's talking flimsy?" Carl replied. "I certainly recommend good rope."

"What else?" I asked, fascinated.

96

"Check it for fraying often," he advised. "Make sure it's fastened to something reliable—something that won't pull loose on you."

"I'm beginning to understand," I said. "Anything else?"

"The first few times, you're bound to get burned a bit," he told me, "from trying to hold on too tight."

"Yeah, I see," I said. Beginning to smell the coffee.

"It'll hurt," Carl continued. "But it won't kill you."

For some reason this conversation made me think of a story I'd read once about the death of the old Queen Elizabeth I. She knew she was dying and didn't like the idea one bit. She was determined to hang on, come hell or high water. Her doctors did what they could, but finally told her she was in the hands of the Lord. In those days, the Lord was still considered to be a man. (There are still some people who consider Him so, especially men.) Anyway, Elizabeth, who had handled lots of men in her time—suitors, advisors, Jesuits, princes, priests, and popes, not to mention armadas—and was generally used to having things her way, was determined to stay alive. Somewhere she had read (according to my source) that the spirit would not leave the body if you remained upright and kept your mouth open. Not being ready to meet the Man, so to speak, she chased her priests out of the room, propped herself upright in a corner and for days remained there, alone, holding onto her tongue until it was purple and swollen. She stayed that way, taking only a little water from her weeping ladies-in-waiting, until finally she fell over dead. Into the arms of the Man, I like to think. I like to think too, that she found Him different from all the other men she'd had to handle all those long years of being queen. I like to think maybe He cooked her some fish like He had for His disciples and maybe multiplied a loaf for her after He healed her swollen tongue.

Thinking about healing and bread reminded me of some things my friend Jeff said about love, about being willing to step outside of security to connect with one another. This, he wrote, is the life of the world that turns our planet from a random collection of atoms into our wonderful home. How it takes courage to let go, to choose the bread of love rather than grasping for the apple that promises immortality, but that actually gives us only a condition of being perpetually undead.

I decided I was sure I didn't want to spend the rest of my life propped in some corner, cozy or otherwise, hanging onto my tongue or my pocketbook or my child or my friends. But I was still puzzled about connecting and letting go. I decided I needed to know more about rappelling.

"I understand about good rope, and connecting it to something that won't pull loose on you, and about burns, and about not holding on too tight," I told Carl. "But," I said, thinking about Elizabeth I, "the odds are pretty good that sometime, well-connected or not, the jigs are going to be up. Am I going to feel like letting go then, or what?"

"If you're very well-connected," Carl answered.

"How do you get that well-connected?" I wondered.

"Practice, my dear," he told me.

"Like with Jeff and Steve?"

"Yes, and Karla."

"Karla," I repeated, without much enthusiasm. "That won't be easy."

"It wasn't all that easy with Jeff and Steve, either," he reminded me.

"That's for sure," I agreed, thinking about how I'd called Steve a turkey and a damn fool in my letter and how, when he replied, he'd only called me "lassie."

"But you weren't standing in a cozy corner holding your tongue. Or chewing your cud," he pointed out. "And I haven't noticed any yaks or woolly mammoths or fire extinguishers on the scene lately, either. And," he continued, "I noticed you didn't grind your teeth or bite the wall when Steve didn't call to say when he was coming. How come?"

"I guess we're well-connected," I laughed. We thought about that for a while. "I guess," I said, "it's when you're afraid of being disconnected that you don't want to let go. That you think you need yaks and woolly mammoths. And fire extinguishers."

"You've come a long way, lassie." he smiled.

"Carl!" I charged. "Have you been reading my mail?"

"Sure have," he admitted.

Taking Your Medicine

As my final round of chemotherapy approached, I found myself thinking many things. For one thing, I seemed to be approaching a kind of milestone. For ten months I'd been going through a process marked off by the very predictable, six-week segments of my treatment. Now it was just about time for the payoff.

My friends and family had been counting too. "We'll have to celebrate!" they said.

"Yes," I agreed, but my heart wasn't in it. I still hated roller coasters. It seemed too soon for celebration. Even if the follow-up tests said everything was okay today, the bottom might fall out tomorrow. To celebrate now would be like whistling in the dark, I felt.

On the other hand, maybe it was enough to celebrate not having to go for six-weekly poisonings—as my friend Jeanne referred to my treatments. Or not having to fill out, file, and follow through on insurance claims. That just might be worth a celebration.

I took my treatments in a five-day series, Monday through Friday, every six weeks. Mondays and Tuesdays were usually a piece of cake. Sometimes by the time I came for Wednesday treatment, I'd have begun to lose my appetite. Thursday through Sunday I'd definitely be feeling like maybe the creek was going to rise. "Sick" was maybe too strong a word for how I'd be feeling. "Discomfort" came a little closer—the kind of discomfort you have just before you have to admit you're about to be seasick. It took nine rounds of treatment before I nailed down exactly the sensation. Everyone has a different experience, the doctors told me. For me, it was the sensation of having a large, sluggish goldfish trying to die in your stomach. Most of the time it would just kind of lie there. But every once in a while, it'd decide to try a sort of swirl, which always ended in an unpleasantly heavy flop. Then it would swim around, stunned-like, for a bit, coming to rest at last, but listing in a morbid sort of way. It would float there until something inspired it to try another swirl. In between swirls, I'd feel a little queasy. Who wouldn't, with a two-pound, half-dead goldfish floating around their insides, threatening to go belly up any minute?

Biofeedback helped. And brisk walks. So did laughing. And deep involvement in conversation or a class discussion or a piece of writing could distract me from the worst of Cleo's (as I came to call the fish) intermittent revivals. Unflavored, kosher yoghurt helped too. I ate a lot of it during my treatment weeks. Several quarts, in fact. A couple teaspoons before meals made it more possible to think of eating with at least some small pleasure. I'd often eat a dishful along with my meals too. It was cold and smooth and soothing to innards traumatized by having their linings eroded, yet expected nevertheless to carry on with their regular duties, despite having to accommodate an outsize, indigestible goldfish.

"You're handling these treatments quite well," Dr. Lefler commented, about round six or seven. "Do you need any more Compazine?"

I told him I wasn't using the Compazine. That I was eating yoghurt instead.

"I've never tried the plain yoghurt," he said politely. He also commented on how nicely my veins were holding up.

"Must be all the vitamins I take," I teased, knowing how nervous doctors are about vitamins. If you can't get your doctor to talk to you about anything other than your bowel habits, just tell him or her that you're on vitamins.

"How many do you take?" Dr. Lefler inquired, fishing for a likely vein for the chemo IV.

"Oh, not that many," I said, stalling for time so he wouldn't miss the vein. When the needle was safely in place and all was to his satisfaction, I dropped the other shoe. "About a handful," I said, casually. His eyebrows shot up.

Dr. Lefler's probably about thirty-five or thirty-six, but looks twentyish, tall, very cute, with short curly blond hair and blue eyes. I remember thinking, the first time I saw him, how he looked like the Understanding Angel in the children's story, *The Littlest Angel.* The one on whose lap the littlest angel sits to explain his unhappiness and dissatisfaction with the lifestyle in Paradise. I wouldn't have been surprised to catch a glimpse of wings, sprouting from his shoulder blades. He did not, however, seem fully aware of his angelic potential. So I dropped yet another shoe.

"Yes." I said. "About a handful of vitamins. Three times a day."

"What do you take?" he inquired.

"Twelve multiple vitamins," I said. "Nine vitamin B complex. Eighteen lecithin. Six beta-carotene. Three vitamin E with selenium. Fifteen vitamin C. Three calcium-magnesium D. Sometimes some alfalfa tabs."

"What brand do you use?" he asked. I told him and he gave his grudging approval.

"Maybe I should take vitamins," he teased me. I usually liked it when he teased me. Normally he was super-professional—confusing in someone with the appearance and demeanor of an Understanding Angel. I wondered how he'd done at medical school in "Zombie I" and "Approximating the Living Dead, I through VI." Not too well, I hoped, though some of those courses had clearly rubbed off on him. Which was a shame. He probably didn't like that much himself.

"What was the hardest thing about medical school for you?" I'd asked him once, trying to get some connecting going. He'd paused, mid-vein, and looked at me.

"Competition," he replied.

"What kind?" I asked.

"Well, first there was the competition to do well enough, make high enough grades to get into medical school," he explained. "Then, once you got in, you didn't want to have the lowest grade point average." He checked to see how the IV bottle was doing, then checked to see if I was following him. He didn't know about my Harvard Ph.D. "Then," he rushed on, "you do your internship. And you don't want to seem the dumbest intern, so you keep on competing. Right up until you graduate."

"Then what?" I asked, glancing at the IV bag to make sure not too many bubbles were coming down. "After all the competing—four years of it in college, four years in med school, another several interning and more if you specialize—what happens then, when you're all comfortably set up in your practice and all the competing suddenly stops?"

"I didn't read another thing in medicine for a year," he told me. "Do you think all that competition was necessary to being a good doctor?" I asked.

"Probably not," he replied, examining my veins again. He was a very gentle man. "They've held up remarkably well," he said. I could tell he was pleased.

"All those vitamins," I reminded him.

"Do you think I ought to take vitamins?" he asked.

"Maybe," I said. "Are you thinking of getting breast cancer?"

"Men can," he said, smiling.

I had about ten or fifteen minutes of thinking to do while the IV ran. Yes, I thought. Men can, but mostly they don't. I corrected myself: very often they don't. (I pride myself on being fair.)

In my experience, men were handicapped in the connecting department. I thought about my father, another doctor who had trouble connecting—until he'd had his heart attack. Then he got better. But by then I was forty-one and had gotten used to his not connecting. When I was in the hospital having my breast removed, he brought me meals he'd cooked himself at home, much of it grown in his garden. I remember especially the vegetable soup, steaming and full of fresh carrots, peas, beans, onions, and fragrant herbs gathered from the garden that morning although it was already fall. There was also homemade bread, a sweet-and-sour gelatin salad, and apple pie. "I'm starving," I'd told him over the phone. "I think they're trying to kill me here." I described the half-cooked pancake and bacon they brought me for breakfast the morning after my surgery. And the cold gelatinous oatmeal. I'd forced it down (except for the bacon), knowing how important nutrition was for cancer patients.

"How was lunch?" my father had asked.

"Equally revolting," I reported. "A clump of something that looked like mousemeat and tasted like something resurrected from the dead. Canned beans, peroxided peaches, potatoes out of a box. The nurses are great, but I don't know if you can live on TLC alone," I worried.

"I'll bring you some dinner," he promised. He did, and I ate it. It tasted wonderful. I felt nourished, and loved. My father wheeled me down for x-rays. He looked them over with the pathologist and told me things looked good. He told me this using all the anatomically correct terms. I understood because he'd always used five-syllable words when he talked to me. The first one I remember very well. I was four. We were walking along the St. Mary's River up in Michigan, on the way to a favorite fishing hole.

"Goddamndemocrats," he'd said.

I thought that was great. "What's a democrat?" I asked hoping to hear more.

He told me all about Democrats, not mincing words. No wonder I grew up to be an English major. I didn't get any of the right genes from my father to go to medical school, or to be a Republican, but, boy, did he teach me to enjoy words. He also taught me to take my medicine. A spanking was administered with no great enthusiasm. He referred to it as a "laying on of hands." The ecclesiastical dimensions of this phrase were not lost on me. Taking your medicine was not something you particularly enjoyed, but, in the long run, it was, according to my father's faith, something that was good for you. It was sure to make you a healthier person than you would be otherwise.

After my surgery I felt so much better than I'd expected to, I thought maybe I could skip the chemotherapy. My oncologist was aghast. He thought I should take my medicine. I supposed he was right and allowed him to adminster it—with no great enthusiasm. It seemed silly to go and take stuff that would make

105

you feel sick after you were beginning to feel really good again. But Dr. Gordon clearly had faith that it would make me a healthier person. And I wanted to be a healthy person, though my faith in chemotherapy was not nearly so great as his. I supplemented it with vitamins. Some counseling. An exercise program. Biofeedback. Meditation and mental imagery. Connectings. Still, when the time came to pull the plug on the chemo, I was uneasy. What if the cancer came flooding back into my body when the poison wore off? I knew the medicine was doing its work attacking fast-growing cells because I lost my hair and there was always good old Cleo to remind me that the cells lining my innards weren't feeling up to snuff. The blood tests also proved that something was happening inside me.

During the week of my final treatment, my friend Margene noted that I didn't seem to be my usual vivacious self. "You were so quiet at lunch," she remarked.

I explained about Cleo. "But this is my last treatment," I told her.

"Ohh! Then the end is in sight!" she rejoiced.

"Yes," I said. "One way or another." She sort of wilted and I was sorry. I apologized. That was not a nice thing to do to a friend. But I just wasn't in a jubilant frame of mind. I did not feel like shoveling out a pony. I decided I'd better have a talk with Carl.

"I'm having trouble with the end of these treatments," I informed him.

"Tell me about it," he encouraged.

"I can prove that the chemo worked," I said. "But now they're stopping. How do I know all the other stuff I've been doing's been working?"

"Like, there's no blood test to prove a connecting?"

"Right," I agreed. Carl always went right to the heart of the matter.

"And you need proof?" he asked.

"Well, it sure would make me feel better," I told him. "I suppose, though, there are some things that can't be proved."

106

"Most things, in fact," he said. "But there are always signs."

"Oh yeah?" I said, dubiously.

"Yes," he assured me. "When your father brought you that feast in the hospital last October, and wheeled you around, and explained the pathologist's report to you, what did you say?" As I said, Carl always goes right to the heart of the matter.

"I said, 'Delicious! Yumm! Best soup I've ever had! Thanks a lot! I really appreciate this!'"

"And what couldn't you say?" Carl pressed. I was quiet for a long time. "What couldn't you say?" he insisted, gently.

"I love you, Daddy," I whispered.

"Can you say 'I love you,' now?"

"Yes," I said.

"That's a sign," he told me. "Sooner or later, the creek's going to rise. For everyone. But you have time. Fill it with love."

I thought about all the love I'd felt since I'd lost my breast—from my friends and family. From Jeff. And Steve. It seemed like more than an even trade.

"Carl," I said. "Thanks. You've really helped me a lot. I really appreciate your help. You're terrific."

"And?" he smiled.

"And...I love you!" I said, "Let's celebrate!"

Letting the Cat out of the Bag

THEY found the cancer in my breast a few days before the university's Homecoming. I was very scared. The doctor, who was from another country, wanted to put me in the hospital and do a biopsy the next day.

"Then what?" I asked.

"Well, I'm afraid it be very bad," he said. "So we might probably have to remove breast. Lymph nodes, too, maybe, under arm. But not very long, you even play golf."

"Really?" I asked, stunned.

"Oh, yes," he assured me. "At first stiff, but then, swing just fine." He gave me a little office demonstration, trying to make me feel better. I didn't have the heart to tell him that I'd never swung just fine. I went back to my office, told Josephine, my boss, and cried. I spent some time with my friend Maurine, talked to my former husband, and made train reservations.

I had decided to go to my parents' home for the biopsy. If it turned out to be very bad, I wanted to be somewhere safe. My father's colleagues, I reasoned, would probably try very hard not to let me die. I also wanted to be sure my son was in good hands while all this was going on. How was I going to explain cancer to him? I wondered.

"Listen," I said to him when he came home from school, "we're going to Wichita Saturday."

"We are?" he said. "Great! How come?"

"Well, I went to the doctor today and he said I might have some bad cells inside me trying to eat up the good cells. I may have to go to the hospital for a while."

"How long?" asked Andrew.

"Oh, maybe a week or so," I told him.

"Who will take care of me?" he cross-examined.

"Grandma and Grandpa."

"Will I stay with them? All day?"

"Yes," I told him.

"Then I won't have to go to school?"

"No. You'll get a little vacation from school."

"Hooray!" he exclaimed.

"Do you have any questions?"

"Can I go tell Peter?"

"Sure," I said. Peter's mom was Maurine and she knew what was cooking.

"When should I come home?" Andrew paused to ask.

"How about five o'clock?"

"Okay. See you later!" He left. I waited for the door to slam, but it didn't.

As I tucked Andrew in bed that night, he was very snuggly. And he had some questions.

"What was wrong with Grandpa?" he wanted to know. His other Grandpa had died of cancer the previous Christmas and he knew it.

"He had cancer," I reminded him.

"He had it for a long time, didn't he?" He'd loved his grandpa a lot.

My father-in-law had had cancer for five years, since Andrew was two.

"Yes," I told him.

110

"Why did he die?" Andrew pressed.

"He was old and tired," I said. "He felt very sick. It isn't easy for your body to get well when you feel that way."

"Children don't get cancer, do they?" he drilled me. I thought I'd better not lie, though I sure wanted to.

"Sometimes," I said. "But children are young and usually healthy and it's easier for them to get better."

"Are we still going to the Homecoming parade tomorrow?" he wanted to know.

"Of course," I reassured him. We'd always gone to the parade, I for fourteen years, Andrew for eight, counting the one he'd attended in utero. I especially remembered the parade when Andrew was eleven months. He'd fallen asleep under my poncho, nursing at my breast, as the trombone section of a particularly enthusiastic band played something like "Colonel Bogie's March." Andrew slept soundly, though there was enough noise to wake the dead. Would there be another Homecoming for me? I wondered. Or was I going to have to settle for a resurrection from the dead? I was more in the mood for trombones than harps.

"After the parade, can we plant the bulbs on Woodstock's grave?" Andrew asked, breaking in upon my eschatological musings. Woodstock, our cat, had died of a brain tumor in August. He was twelve. When he got sick, seeing the writing on the wall, I'd read Judith Viorst's *Ten Good Things About Barney*, a good book about a family whose cat dies, aloud to Andrew. I'd cried, reading it, but it hadn't seemed to impress Andrew at the time.

"How come you're crying, Mom?" he'd asked.

"It makes me feel sad," I'd said.

"It's just a story," he'd reassured me.

All the children in the neighborhood came over to help us plant the bulbs. Andrew supervised, and told the kids all about Woodstock.

"He was my cat and he really loved me," he said. "He sat on my lap. He never bit or scratched. Once he ate half a mouse under the dining room table. My mom found the other half."

"Yuk!" laughed all the children.

"And he was very soft," he said, and the kids got quiet.

"But when he was dead, he was hard as a rock," he informed them, rapping his trowel on a log for emphasis.

The cat had died at the vet's in August while we were away on vacation. Andrew visited him before we left and snuggled him in his arms as the vet and I exchanged glances. Woodstock, Dr. Loop and I thought, was well on his way to cat heaven. He died before we returned and Dr. Loop black-bagged him and put him in his freezer. It was not much fun going to collect that black bag. I cried in the vet's office and all the way home. He'd been my pet for a long time. I cried while I dug a grave in the garden. The weather was very hot and humid. The soil was as hard as the frozen cat. I thought about how much I was going to miss Woodstock. "But thank God it's a cat, not a St. Bernard," I found myself thinking. "Or a pony."

I brought Andrew home from the neighbor's and told him Woodstock had died.

"No!" he cried, and hit me—hard.

We sat down in the white chair and hugged each other and cried together.

"But I loved him. He can't be dead. I don't want him dead," Andrew protested. "Why?" There was no easy answer, so we just cried some more. Finally Andrew wondered, "Where is he now?"

"Out in the garden," I said, sidestepping the question of cat heaven. "Would you like to help me bury him?"

"Yes," he said, with an alacrity that surprised me. I showed him the grave and the black bag. I helped him line the grave with grass and soft branches and then placed the bundle gently in the ground.

"Shall we put some more grass on top?" I asked cheerfully, praying like crazy, "Dear God, don't let him want to open the bag, please don't let him want to open the bag." I knew I'd cry some more if I had to look at Woodstock. I didn't want to cry anymore. Andrew collected some grass and I began to crumble dirt over the bag.

"Mom," Andrew interrupted me. I pretty well knew what was coming.

"Mom, why are we leaving him in the bag?"

I knew that if I gave him a sensible-sounding answer in my knowing-mother, matter of fact, that's-the-way-we-do-it voice, he wouldn't protest.

I could say something like, "Well, the bag will keep him from getting all nasty and dirty" or "The city likes for animals to be buried in bags" or even, with firmness, "I think it would be best."

As Andrew waited for my answer, I appealed to the Lord. "It would only be a small lie," I said. "Why make this any more upsetting than it already is? We wouldn't want a little boy to start crying all over again, would we?" I reasoned. "Besides, who knows what the cat's going to look like now," I pointed out. "What if it's frozen in a final death agony? What if its eyes are bugging out, its tongue protruding, its face a ghoulish grimace?" I wanted the Lord to be sure to have the whole picture. I was sure the Lord would not want Andrew to remember his cat that way.

"How come, Mom?" Andrew interrupted my struggle with the truth. The George Washington in me won. Or maybe it was the Lord.

"Do you really want to look at him?" I asked, still hoping that maybe he wouldn't.

He did, though, so I hauled the plastic bundle up out of the hole, untwisted the fastener and gently took the cat out of the bag. And cried. Not so much because of the cat, this time, but because of the kindness of Dr. Loop. Before Woodstock had had a chance to stiffen, the vet had curled him up in a ball, one ear resting on his paws, chin tilted up, tail almost but not quite touching his nose. I stroked him and was glad I hadn't lied about cats in bags. Andrew picked him up, looked in his face, and put him back on the ground. He made a fist and rapped on him.

"Hard," he said.

113

"Yes," I agreed, rapping him myself. "Shall we bury him now?"

"Okay. Can I do it?"

"Sure," I said. It took about half an hour. I was glad, once more, that Woodstock was not a St. Bernard. Afterwards, we went in, washed the dirt off and drank some lemonade.

"What will happen to him now?" Andrew wanted to know. I didn't think he wanted to hear about cat heaven.

"You mean, what will happen to his body in the ground?" I asked.

"Yeah. What will happen to it?"

"It will turn into dirt and make the flowers grow better," I told him. "In the fall, we'll plant some bulbs here, if you want."

"Yes. Will his fur turn to dirt?"

"Yes."

"What about his teeth?"

"His teeth too."

"His eyes?"

"Uh-huh."

"Claws?"

"Yes."

"All of him?"

"All of him."

"Woodstock was pretty old, wasn't he?"

"Yes. For a cat," I told him.

"I'm hungry. What's there to eat?"

As I packed to go to the hospital, Andrew wandered in and out of the room. Finally he squatted beside me.

"Just what are they going to do to you?" he wanted to know.

114

"Well," I said, "you know what I said about the bad cells trying to eat the good cells?"

"Uh-huh."

"Most of the bad cells seem to be in my left breast. So what they're going to do is give me a shot to put me to sleep...."

"Peter said they're going to cut off your breast," he said.

"Yes," I said.

"Will it hurt?" he asked.

"No, I'll be asleep."

"Then the bad cells will all be gone, right?"

"We hope so. They'll probably give me some medicine afterwards just to make sure."

"You don't need a breast anymore 'cause you're through nursing your kid, right?"

"Right!"

"What will they do with it?"

"I don't know. Maybe they'll put it in a jar for me."

"Oh, Mom!" he laughed.

As it turned out, I was only in the hospital three and a half days. Andrew and I talked on the phone. My mother or father would take me downstairs in a wheelchair, IV's and all, and Andrew would sit on my lap and eat ice cream with me. He seemed cheerful enough. I breathed a sigh of relief, even though they'd found that my breast and armpit were stuffed with cancer.

A week later, though, my brother Fred, who had taken Andrew out on his construction jobs while I was recuperating, invited me on a walk. "Just what have you told Andrew about this?" he asked. "Not a whole lot," I said, "but he doesn't seem to be worrying particularly."

"He sure gave me the third degree today," said my brother. "He asked me how old you were and wanted to know if that was old for a mom. Then he told me that his grandpa who was old had died of cancer and wanted to know if all grown-ups with cancer died of it."

It looked as if this cat would have to come out of the bag too.

"Andrew," I said, when I got home, "do you have questions about cancer you'd like to ask me?"

"Like what?" he hedged. I could tell this was not going to be easy.

"Cancer is a pretty serious illness."

"Yes. Grandpa died of it. And Woodstock. I was wondering why you didn't die of it," he admitted.

"I'm younger. And healthier," I said.

"Do you still have it?"

"Yes."

"What will happen to me if you die?" I told him what the arrangements were. "But I'm not planning to die anytime real soon."

"I wish you'd never gotten cancer." he said.

"Me too," I agreed.

"I wish people didn't die." he said. "Or animals. I wish we could all just go on living forever. I mean in this world. I know we live forever in heaven."

"It would get pretty crowded in this world if no one died," I said. "And when you're very sick a lot of times you don't feel like living in this world anymore."

"Woodstock couldn't even purr anymore when he was sick," Andrew remembered. "I notice you seem to be feeling pretty good."

"Right now," I said, "I feel purr-fectly good!"

"Oh, Mom!" he laughed.

A while later I overheard him lecturing a row of assorted stuffed animals on cancer and cats and death. "And when you're real sick, all you want is to go to heaven, see? And there wouldn't

116

be room if no one died. If she died, I'd go to live with the Joswicks." There was a pause. And then, "But I still wish she hadn't got cancer."

The cat was out of the bag and it was hard all right. "Lord," I prayed as I tiptoed away, "I wish I didn't have cancer, too. But thanks for this sweet, honest child."

Cinnamon Rolls and Rocket Ships

WHEN you're living with cancer, you never know what's around the corner. You never know, even if you don't have cancer, but you're not so aware of the corners. Nearly two years after my surgery and six months after the end of my treatments, the radiologist didn't like the looks of something on my spine. I could tell by the way Julie, the receptionist, handed me a gown and fled that something was up. Dr. Veeder came in and told me about it.

I reminded him that I had a nine-year-old to raise. He remembered about that. He was not happy that this turned up.

"We'd better get a bone scan," he said.

"Then what?" I wanted to know. "More chemo, I suppose."

"Yes," admitted Dr. Veeder.

"Same kind as before or different?"

"Different." He told me the kind and the side effects. This time I'd be bald as a billiard ball. It didn't do the heart any good either. I didn't ask about vomiting. I didn't want to know. I felt like a can of spinach—drained, yellowish-green, mushy.

I'd decided to learn how to be a counselor so I went to my counseling class afterwards. No one seemed to notice that there was a can of spinach in the room. After an hour or so, I started to participate and, by the end of class, I was feeling better.

"How'd things go?" I asked my baby sitter when I returned home.

Turned out my usually sweet son had tried to kick her to pieces. "He's under a lot of stress right now," I told her. She seemed to understand. I went to bed thinking about the bone scan. And thinking how a can of spinach wasn't all that much use to a nine-year-old.

I liked Don, the radiologist. He didn't say much, but he looked at me when he spoke. He didn't seem to see a can of spinach. Or a potentially dead person. I listened to the machine clicking. Someone had told me when the clicks were evenly spaced, things were fine. Lots of clicks all in a row, though, meant trouble. "Click," went the machine. "Click...click...click." I began to breathe more freely. But then "click-click-click-click-clickety-click-click," went the machine. Jesus Christ, I thought.

Don brought the pictures out into the hospital corridor where I was sitting. He sat down in a chair beside me and showed them to me.

"There's nothing here," he said, and smiled.

"Nothing." I repeated. "But—" I was going to ask about the clicks. Just then a white-coated technician bustled out of the lab with a handful of forms.

"Click," went the little time clock. "Click. Clickclickclick-clickclick," it went as the technician got the hang of it better.

"Nothing," I said again and laughed—hysterically. Don laughed too. I wanted to explain about the clicks but no words would come.

"Julie sent your book over," he told me and handed me the book I'd forgotten in my misery when I left the doctor's office the day before. I thanked him, walked over to thank Julie and give her the good news. She was very pleased. Then I went straight to the travel agent and bought plane tickets to Florida for Easter vacation. I'd been putting it off too long, I decided. I swam in the ocean and walked on the beach with Kathy, my sister. Andrew and his cousin Becki made sand castles.

Three months later the same thing happened. A suspicious place on my spine, more bone scans. I called my friend Elvy. She came right over to listen to me. She hugged me when I cried. She went with me for the bone scan. Good news again. I relaxed,

120

went home for a high school reunion. This time, though, I couldn't forget about the clickclickclicks.

There was a message on my answering machine asking me to call Dr. Veeder when I returned. I couldn't believe it. He and the pathologist didn't agree. I should come in on Thursday and talk about it. He thought I should have my spine examined. With a needle this time. I said some fairly unpleasant things, I recall.

"I'm sorry," he said.

"That's okay," I whispered.

"I can't stand it," I howled to Wanda who was there cleaning my house. "First up, then down. It's awful. I feel like just throwing in the towel. Seems like it's going to get me one time or another," I raved. Wanda let me. I was glad she was there. Finally, I subsided.

After a decent interval, Wanda observed, "You know, they say the Lord never closes one door but He opens another." We both reflected on that for a bit. "Sometimes, though," Wanda broke the silence, "seems like He's misplaced my handle."

That's exactly how I felt. Like no one had a hold of me. The handle to me was lost or broken off. I was heading back into the world of the potentially dead. Back to wigs, being sick on chemotherapy, being different again—just as I was beginning to be the same.

"Poor Anne," my friends would be saying. "She's putting up a good fight, but it'll probably get her anyway. Just a matter of time."

"I can't stand it!" I reiterated to Wanda.

"What are you going to do?" she asked.

Do? That's right. I could still do something. And I did. My friend Ethel made me an appointment with Dr. Carbone in Wisconsin and drove me there. She told me about her sister-in-law who had died of breast cancer and who had wanted to stay sexy and beautiful. We talked about our lives and enjoyed the misty hills of Wisconsin. I began to feel better. Jeff had called before I left. He said he'd be doing some heavyshit praying. He said he loved me. That made me feel better too. And braver.

I was glad I went to Wisconsin. Ethel had told me how kind and smart and capable Dr. Carbone was. He also, I found, was not afraid of connecting. While I sulked grimly on the edge of the examining table, he took my case history himself.

He asked about my teaching and my child. How was I feeling? he inquired.

Healthwise, fine, I told him. Otherwise, upset. Scared to death. I complained about chemo and wigs and roller coasters and feeling potentially dead again. I watched to see how he was taking this.

He didn't seem surprised. "I'd be scared too," he told me. He spent an hour and a half with me. He introduced me to his colleagues, who talked with me and tested me and discussed results. He showed me pictures of his grandchild. He carried my bookbag. I could tell he didn't think I was a can of spinach. Or a potentially dead person.

I was not, it turned out, sick again. This time. I was glad—but back home, away from the magic of Dr. Carbone and the taste of the good life with Ethel and her husband Laurie, the fear came seeping back. I dreaded going for my pap smear: what if it showed more cancer? I hated my answering machine now: someday I might turn it on and find a message from a doctor's office.

"This is your doctor's office speaking," I might hear. "Due to a computer error your records were confused with those of a Ms. Ima Gonner. You are not well after all. Please contact our office at your earliest convenience. We will be happy to help you calculate how many days you have left in this world. You might also be interested in our new pay-as-you-go hospice plan."

I got farther behind in everything, more tired (probably just the inevitable leukemia setting in). I tried living one day at a time. I tried burying myself in detective novels. I tried Scotch.

Just at sunrise one morning as I finished up my daily walk, I watched Amtrak speed throught the cornfields on its way into town and then on north. I thought about how I'd always liked being on trains. Going somewhere. A good feeling. You check the schedule, get on the right train, relax and enjoy the ride. If you want to go somewhere else, you check things out and change trains. Eventually you get to the right place. I'd been missing that feeling. I decided to compare notes with Carl. I preferred trains to roller coasters, I told him.

"Trains sometimes get sidetracked," he reminded me. "Or derailed."

"I don't want to get derailed," I told him. "But when I think of starting something, this likeitizzard starts in."

"This what?" queried Carl.

"Likeitizzard," I repeated. "It's the thing that crawls out from behind your liver when things seem to be going quite nicely and tells it like it is."

"And how is it?" Carl asked. "We haven't talked for a while."

"Rotten," I said. "One day at a time doesn't work for me. I need to know I'm going somewhere."

"You're feeling like doing something's no good unless you can finish it?"

"Exactly," I agreed.

"Let's think about cinnamon rolls," he suggested.

It didn't seem too promising a topic, but this was my Inner Guide suggesting it. So I closed my eyes, curled up in my white chair, and thought about cinnamon rolls. I thought about the cinnamon rolls my mother had baked by the gross—how warm and spicy they were and how we used to devour them and begin wishing for more. How there never seemed to be enough. I thought about the cinnamon rolls my friend Barbara and I had eaten together. Brobdidnagian rolls baked up at T. J. Cinnamon's shop in Kansas City that you could smell all the way to Olathe.

"Carl," I said. "Have you ever been in a T. J. Cinnamon's?"

"That the place you can smell all the way to Olathe?"

"Yes. Barbara and I ate there once. I ate all of my roll. Barbara ate only part of hers."

"Really?" Carl replied. "She didn't finish it? Jeez, must not've been worth starting. That half must not've tasted very good to her—thinking about the other half she wasn't going to be able to eat..."

"Oh shut up, Carl," I interrupted.

"And I bet she just threw that uneaten part in the trash bin," he continued. " 'If I can't eat it, no one can,' I'll bet she reasoned."

"Cut it out," I said. "As a matter of fact, I think she took it home to Jeff."

"So it wasn't all up to her to finish it then?"
"I guess not," I agreed. "But life's not a cinnamon roll."

"Really?"

"Really. When you're alive you like to explore and create. And grow. Everywhichway."

"And see how it all turns out?"

"And see how it all turns out."

We thought about that for a while. I thought about all the things I wanted to see turn out. Andrew, my son, for instance. How good a teacher I could get to be. And counselor, maybe. And writer. Who else I'd find to love.

"If there were such a thing," asked Carl, "would you like a crystal ball?"

"No. It wouldn't be quite the same. I'd want to be there."

We were quiet some more. I thought of all the other people who'd probably wanted to see how things turned out. Being a teacher and all, I found myself thinking of Christa McAuliff. Andrew and I had sat in the white chair and watched her spaceship explode in the curved glass of the television screen. Watched it veer crazily off its carefully planned trajectory. Watched the billowing smoke spelling the end to so many people's dreams and loves across the bright Florida sky. I remembered watching an elementary school teacher talking to her class about the terrible sight they'd witnessed.

"Lots of us are probably thinking maybe Christa should have stayed home," said the teacher.

"Yeah!" said some of the children.

"Didn't Christa have a dream?" asked the teacher.

"Yes," said all the kids.

"Isn't a dream something we all need to have?" she asked them.

"Yes!" they agreed.

"If you have a dream, shouldn't you follow it, shouldn't you be on your way? Even if it means taking a risk?"

"Yes," they agreed once more.

"And wasn't Christa on her way?"

"Carl," I said, "I'm on my way."

"Everywhichway," he smiled.

About the Author

Anne C. Hargrove received her B.A. from Indiana University, her Ph.D. from Harvard University, and is now working toward a degree in counseling. She is Professor of English at Western Illinois University, where she teaches writing and literature. Her special field is Shakespeare, and she has helped with the university's Shakespearean productions. She has also done academic advising.

Anne's cancer was diagnosed when she was forty-one, recently divorced, and raising an eight-year-old on her own. She wrote the first chapter in this book two weeks after her mastectomy, and continued to write about her illness and recovery over a two-year period, until the twenty-five chapters were complete. "I began to write as self-therapy," she explains, "but suspected that my essays could help others like me, as well as relatives, counselors, pastors, and friends of those living through cancer."

Getting Better is her first non-academic publication, but she also has written a book on counseling and is working on collections of short stories and poetry. She and her son, Andrew, live in Macomb, Illinois, with their two cats and a dog.

Resources

Books

Achterberg, Jeanne. *Imagery in Healing: Shamanism and Modern Medicine*. Boston: Shambhala: New Science Library, 1985.

Borysenko, Joan, Ph.D. *Minding the Body, Mending the Mind*. Reading, Mass.: Addison-Wesley, 1987.

Cousins, Norman. *Anatomy of an Illness as Perceived by the Patient*. New York: Norton, 1979; New York: Bantam, 1981.

———. *The Healing Heart*. New York: Avon, 1984.

Dyer, Wayne W. *Gifts From Eykis*. New York: Simon and Schuster: Pocket Books, 1983.

———. *Pulling Your Own Strings*. New York: Avon, 1978.

———. *Your Erroneous Zones*. New York: Avon, 1977.

Fromm, Erich. *The Art of Loving*. New York: Harper and Row, 1974.

Gaes, Jason. *My Book for Kids with Cancer*. Aberdeen, South Dakota: Melius and Peterson, 1987.

Gawain, Shakti. *Creative Visualization*. New York: Bantam, 1985.

Goble, Frank. *The Third Force*. New York: Simon and Schuster: Pocket Books, 1971.

Jampolsky, Gerald, M.D. *Love Is Letting Go of Fear*. Berkeley, Calif.: Celestial Arts, 1979.

———. *Teach Only Love: The Seven Principles of Attitudinal Healing*. New York: Bantam, 1983.

Kalter, Suzy. *Looking Up: The Complete Guide to Looking and Feeling Good for the Recovering Cancer Patient*. New York: McGraw-Hill, 1987.

Kauffman, Danette G. *Surviving Cancer*. Washington, D.C.: Acropolis Books, 1987.

Koller, Alice. *An Unknown Woman: A Journey to Self-Discovery*. New York: Holt, Rinehart and Winston, 1982.

Kubler-Ross, Elisabeth. *On Death and Dying*. New York: Macmillan, 1969.

Kushner, Harold S. *When Bad Things Happen to Good People*. New York: Schocken, 1981; New York: Avon, 1983.

Kushner, Rose. *Alternatives: New Developments in the War on Breast Cancer*. New York: Warner Books, Inc., with the Kensington Press, Cambridge, Mass., 1984.

Lakein, Alan. *How to Get Control of Your Time and Your Life*. New York: Signet, 1973.

Levenson, Frederick B. *The Causes and Prevention of Cancer*. New York: Stein and Day, 1985.

Lindbergh, Anne M. *Gift from the Sea*. New York: Pantheon, 1955.

Lingerman, Hal. *The Healing Energies of Music*. Wheaton, Ill.: Theosophical Publishing House, 1983.

Locke, Stephen, M.D. *The Healer Within*. Mentor, 1987.

Merton, Thomas. *Conjectures of a Guilty Bystander*. New York: Doubleday, 1968.

―――. *Asian Journals*. New York: New Directions, 1973.

―――. *New Seeds of Contemplation*. New York: New Directions, 1972.

Nouwen, Henri. *Reaching Out*. New York: Doubleday, 1986.

―――. *With Open Hands*. New York: Ballantine, 1985.

Peck, M. Scott, M.D. *The Road Less Traveled*. New York: Simon and Schuster, 1978.

Pelletier, Kenneth R. *Mind as Healer, Mind as Slayer: A Holistic Approach to Preventing Stress Disorders*. New York: Dell, 1977. Seamands, David A. *Healing of Memories*. Wheaton, Ill.: Victor Books, 1985.

Siegel, Bernie S., M.D. *Love, Medicine and Miracles: Lessons Learned about Self-Healing from a Surgeon's Experience with Exceptional Patients*. New York: Harper and Row, 1987.

Simons, George F. *Keeping Your Personal Journal*. Mahwah, N.J.: Paulist Press, 1978.

Simonton, O. Carl, and Stephanie Matthew Simonton. *Getting Well Again*. New York: Bantam, 1984.

Simonton-Atchley, Stephanie. *The Healing Family*. New York: Bantam, 1986.

Solzhenitsyn, Aleksandr. *Cancer Ward*, trans. Nicolas Bethel and David Berg. New York: Farrar, Straus and Giroux, 1969; New York: Bantam, 1969.

Tournier, Paul. *The Meaning of Persons*. New York: Harper and Row, 1957.

Viorst, Judith. *Ten Good Things About Barney*. New York: Atheneum, 1971.

Periodicals

Cope. A magazine published ten times a year for health professionals. Denver, Colo.: Pulse Publications.

Coping: Living with Cancer. A magazine published quarterly for patients living with cancer. Denver, Colo.: Pulse Publications.